HANDBOOK OF FATIGUE
TESTING

Sponsored by ASTM Committee E-9
on Fatigue

ASTM SPECIAL TECHNICAL PUBLICATION 566
S. Roy Swanson, Editor

List price $17.25
04-566000-30

AMERICAN SOCIETY FOR TESTING AND MATERIALS
1916 Race Street, Philadelphia, Pa. 19103

NOTE

The Society is not responsible, as a body,
for the statements and opinions
advanced in this publication.

Printed in Baltimore, Md.
October 1974

Foreword

In 1949 Committee E-9 on Fatigue published *ASTM STP 91, Manual of Fatigue Testing*. The project leading to *STP 91* involved the specific writing of eight members of E-9 and the discussions and criticisms of members of the main committee over a period of three years. *STP 91* was a modest effort and succeeded in presenting what was then considered to be the current practice and views of E-9 members.

The present *Handbook of Fatigue Testing* is the culmination of an extensive attempt to survey and document the broad facets of fatigue testing. Subject matter was provided by a large number of E-9 members to an editorial group initially headed by Foster B. Stulen and Professor S. M. Marco, both of whom are now deceased. Consolidation of this input has been completed under the editorship of Dr. S. Roy Swanson, with some major changes in emphasis. The reader will find a definite attempt to discuss fatigue machines, test techniques, and associated equipment that can satisfy the requirements of a modern research person or test engineer. More often than not, their needs reflect the desire to test material, components, and structures under conditions that clearly simulate service loading and environments.

As Chairman of Committee E-9, I am grateful for the time and effort that Dr. Swanson put into completing this handbook. I am also grateful to those individuals specifically cited in the Editor's brief Preface.

W. S. Hyler, Chairman
ASTM Committee E-9 on Fatigue

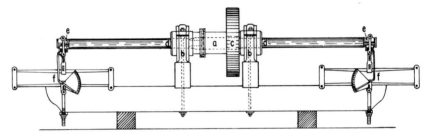

Zeitschr. f. Bauwesen 1860

Apparat zum Probiren der Widerstandsfähigkeit
von Wagen-Achsen gegen wiederholte Biegungen.

Wöhler's machine for fatigue testing of railway axles.

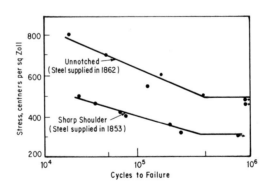

Wöhler's S-N curves for Krupp axle steel.

Preface

This handbook contains contributions from a large number of ASTM Committee E-9 members. My task has been to take this information and distill it into a unified theme. Because of my background and interests, the unified theme embraces fatigue testing under simulated loading conditions. For this reason, there is considerable emphasis on servocontrolled fatigue test systems and allied equipment. This concentration on modern equipment appears to be particularly important for the young research worker or test engineer, since it is this sort of equipment to which he will be introduced.

I should like to recognize with special gratitude those individuals who have spent long hours reviewing and criticizing the various drafts. Specifically, I would like to thank John Bennett, Ron Broderick, Horace Grover, Herbert Hardrath, Walter Hyler, Harold Reemsnyder, and Dick Thurston. These gentlemen formed the review board which has guided my efforts over the past few years.

S. Roy Swanson
Editor

Related
ASTM Publications

Manual on Low Cycle Fatigue Testing, STP 465 (1970), $12.50, 04-465000-30

Cyclic Stress-Strain Behavior—Analysis, Experimentation, and Fatigue Prediction, STP 519 (1973), $28.00, 04-519000-30

Fatigue at Elevated Temperatures, STP 520 (1973), $45.50, 04-520000-30

Contents

Chapter 1—Introduction

1.1 Purpose

Over the past quarter-century, since the *Manual on Fatigue Testing, ASTM STP 91* was published, the study of materials fatigue has grown to such an extent, that following only one of its ramifications can be the lifework of a large number of researchers. Materials fatigue is a hybrid science, having to draw heavily on several traditional sciences, such as metallurgy, statistics, and dynamic analysis. Rarely does one hear of a student studying "Fatigue Engineering" or some such direct approach to the problem. It is more likely that the researcher's background was one of the supporting sciences. For this reason, the present *Handbook of Fatigue Testing* was prepared as a source of information for the person who finds himself becoming a fatigue engineer.

Fatigue strength is probably the most quality-sensitive of the engineering properties, because the imperfections of real-life processes have a vital effect on the fatigue performance of the material. Man's inability to manufacture the material perfectly (flawlessly, free of residual stresses, etc.); his inability to fabricate the structures from the materials without using somewhat primitive joining methods, involving geometrical and metallurgical notches, etc.; and finally, his inability to define completely the environment (loadings, etc.) that the structure must experience in its lifetime—all these inabilities accumulate their uncertainties to cause the problems associated with fatigue life prediction.

It is necessary, however, to know something of the nature of fatigue in order to plan and conduct tests intelligently. Fatigue failures generally start as minute surface cracks which grow under the action of a fluctuating stress until a dominant crack attains critical size, causing failure. The stress necessary to initiate fatigue cracks is often less than that required to cause gross plastic deformation of the material. There is often little relief of the stress concentration at discontinuities, and cracks will generally start at such stress-raisers. Because of the inhomogeneity of real-life materials, this usually results in a wide dispersion of fatigue test results from nominally identical specimens and conditions. This fact must be kept in mind from the initial design of the fatigue experiment to the final evaluation of the test results.

Fatigue tests are conducted for a wide variety of purposes and the specimens tested range all the way from tiny samples of thin foil to complete aircraft weighing many tons. This handbook will point out the principles and techniques of fatigue testing, so that the reader will be assisted in defining his problem accurately, choosing an effective testing method, avoiding pitfalls in conducting the test program, and evaluating the results realistically.

1.2 Scope

No attempt will be made in this handbook to cover areas outside the general area of fatigue testing. Complete books (and indeed several manuals) have now been written on specific aspects of material fatigue (for example, low cycle fatigue, fatigue at elevated temperature, etc.).

By restricting the scope to testing itself, it is possible to attempt an in-depth study of testing that will be reasonably up-to-date at the time of publication. Such an objective is absolutely essential in a field that is changing as fast as that of fatigue testing. Gone are the days when very simple questions such as, "Will it stand one million constant amplitude (rotating beam) load reversals?" are asked of the fatigue engineer. Now he is asked to determine the actual fatigue life, often under complex service conditions. For this reason, this handbook may appear rather different from earlier manuals.

While material fatigue behavior in itself is not studied in this manual, there remains the question, "How is the fatigue resistance of materials most usefully characterized?" To answer this question, careful judgement has to be exercised in the selection of the test method, the specimen, and the procedure appropriate to the situation, so that the designer avoids the generation of test data not relevant to his purposes. In this sense, knowledge of material fatigue behavior has guided the writing of the manual.

In the present decade, the field of fatigue testing is seen to be rapidly maturing. The earlier years can be looked upon as a time when fatigue testing suffered from an isolation from many disciplines which could have helped it to develop at a faster rate. To name but a few of these disciplines, one would include servocontrol, electronics, digital techniques and computer science, and transducer (sensor) technology. Of course, these fields were rapidly developing themselves. Presently, however, fatigue testing is flourishing from its ability to incorporate new developments in these related primary fields, almost as quickly as they are introduced.

This handbook contains illustrative descriptions of several types of equipment, of important concerns in specimen design and preparation, and of items important in monitoring tests and recording test data. In describing equipment, it was not feasible to include actual details of the immense variety of testing equipment presently available, nor of all the special tests that are conducted for various reasons. Rather, the emphasis is upon principles in the "art" of fatigue testing, so that the engineer can choose wisely among alternatives available to him and appropriate to his objectives.

The layout of the handbook has been organized so that the inexperienced fatigue test engineer can obtain the information he needs to carry out his test with the degree of precision and care pertinent to his objective. Early emphasis is placed on the necessity to design the experiment carefully. Then a consideration of the test apparatus required is given, then the design of the specimen, and incorporation of an environment. The references at the end of each chapter are related to the testing topic of that chapter.

It is recognized that the scope of activity in fatigue is so great at present, that no single source can call itself definitive. Indeed, many standing professional committees and government bodies throughout the world are continuously at work on the problem of generating standards, specifications, norms for fatigue testing. Appendix C will indicate as many of the groups as possible so that the reader can look into their work further, if he desires.

Consideration should be given to the social impact of the technical discipline of fatigue testing. There is a very definite social responsibility on the part of those who manufacture products for man's use, that they be safe to use either indefinitely or for a specified lifetime. Fatigue testing plays a key role in estimating this lifetime and thus can lead to better product reliability. For this reason, the potential user of this handbook must realize that carefully controlled tests and service simulation can be achieved with equipment available today, so that reasonable estimates of fatigue behavior of materials and products can be obtained. Of course, much fatigue research is involved very indirectly with the social problem of structural integrity (for example, fundamental studies of pure materials, etc.), and requirements in this area also will be covered. It is probably no exaggeration, at the present time, to state that fatigue testing capability has actually advanced beyond the imagination of many workers in the fatigue field. The main limitation now is essentially one of economics.

Chapter 2—Considerations in the Design of the Fatigue Test Program

2.1 Introduction

At some point in time, the research worker in fatigue or the fatigue engineer will be confronted with the requirement to devise a fatigue test program in answer to a specific need or technical challenge. This need, or challenge, may be as simple as developing information about the fatigue behavior of material as influenced by composition, microstructure, processing factors, environmental influences, etc., well in advance of specific end use definition. It may involve the continued search to develop empirical fatigue rules (or theories) which can be utilized with confidence in the design process. It may also involve the evaluation of structural parts and full-scale assemblies under conditions that simulate the many combinations of varying and steady loads to which such structures may be subjected in service.

Whatever the scope, need, or challenge, there are certain considerations that must be thought through in this process of designing a test program. This chapter presents a discussion of these considerations which consists of the following:

1. *General Planning* which encompasses the establishment of objectives, considers constraints, and focuses on cost factors.
2. *Test Program Design* which involves a consideration of the structure of the program, the loading and environmental variables, and the specimen design.
3. *Conduct of the Program* which involves the establishment of all test procedures and an evaluation of limitations.
4. *Presentation of the Data* which includes both analysis and reporting.

Following presentation of this material, the chapter concludes with discussions of two types of multilaboratory test programs. One of these is identified as multilaboratory data-generation programs; the other, as interlaboratory test programs.

2.2 General Planning

Although this section contains the word "planning" in the title, it is not the only major section to be concerned with planning. Sections 2.3, 2.4, and 2.5 also involve planning of the experiment. General planning implies the establishment of the scope or breadth of the program and involves the establishment of realistic objectives, an appraisal of constraints, and an estimate of cost.

2.2.1 Objectives

A fatigue test is undertaken to satisfy an objective, or set of objectives, defined by the test planner after he has reviewed the literature and assessed previous experiments in light of his needs. It is important that the objectives be carefully and clearly specified for all concerned. There are several different objectives for fatigue investigations:

1. to develop basic understanding about the fatigue behavior of materials,
2. to extend empirical knowledge about the fatigue behavior of materials,
3. to obtain information on the fatigue response of a component, and
4. to obtain information concerning the behavior of a component or structure under service loadings.

Often, it will not be possible to satisfy a number of objectives with a single type of test. Laboratory tests on materials specimens, for instance, will not be expected to provide information entirely adequate for structural design, since the specimens do not include all the factors of fabrication and assembly that are known to affect the fatigue of structures. Even notched specimens seldom represent all the stress raisers, residual stresses, and surface conditions that may exist in structures. Accordingly, specimens for developing information on materials are usually designed to be simple, reproducible, and as inexpensive as possible. Examples of specimen design and preparation are given in Chapter 6.

Even within this framework of simplicity, there are subobjectives which influence the detailed planning. For example, in material fatigue, the subobjectives may be one of the following.

Comparative Testing of Several Materials—Comparison of the fatigue behavior of one material with another frequently is limited to involving (1) one type of loading, (2) one load ratio, (3) one environment, (4) one condition of heat treatment, surface finish, etc. It is important, in comparative testing, not to extrapolate the results from one type of loading to another nor to other environments. For example, low-stress, constant-amplitude tests will not always indicate the same comparative fatigue strength for several materials that subsequently are tested under variable-amplitude loading, where stress interaction can be expected. This should be particularly expected if the constant amplitude S-N curves for two materials would intersect each other.

Effect of Processing—To evaluate the effect on fatigue behavior of processing factors the real objective is often limited to comparisons of fatigue behavior of two or three sets of specimens with different heat treatments or surface or other production processing (for example, forging process variables, hole preparation techniques, etc.).

Environmental Effects—To evaluate special effects of stressing or environment, the more limited realistic goal is again comparison of fatigue lifetimes of a few sets of specimens under a few different conditions that simulate environments (corrosive or temperature) expected in service.

Effect of Geometric Discontinuities—To evaluate effects on fatigue behavior of geometric discontinuities may involve a limited goal to study a few typical notch shapes, each with a limited range either of K_t or radius, r (as defined in Appendix A).

In each of the listed subobjectives, rather limited but typical, scopes have been suggested. In the general planning stage, it is necessary to consider how extensively such limited data may be extrapolated. Such consideration may provide the basis for broadening the scope of a program.

Fatigue investigations of a structural part or component may have slightly different subobjectives:

1. to determine the fatigue resistance of a part or component under loading and environmental conditions akin to service conditions,
2. to explore the advantages of using different materials or processing and fabricating practices, and
3. to assess differences in fatigue behavior that may arise from real design changes.

Complete structures and structural assemblies are usually investigated to estimate service reliability. This implies a simulated service loading in contrast to many tests of materials specimens and even of component parts. There may, however, still be varied objectives. For example:

1. to determine modes of failure under some specified loading,
2. to determine relative lifetimes under somewhat varied loadings (for example, different load spectra), and
3. to establish realistic inspection intervals for structures involved in service and to establish realistic lifetime limits.

The more complex a structure and the more complex the loading, the more expensive is a single test. Hence, it becomes particularly important to consider the objectives as realistically as possible.

2.2.2 Constraints

The establishment of broad program objectives and more limited subobjectives, as just described, probably is carried out as an iterative process. The iterations involve objectives, detailed plans, and constraints. While there may be technical factors which will limit an investigator's program plan, as brought out in a later section, the chief constraints to any fatigue investigation will be the time available to accomplish a piece of work and the resultant cost. Both of these factors dramatically influence the content and plan of a fatigue program, usually in a fairly direct way. This is particularly so when the program is only a part of a broader developmental program; that is, a new high-temperature alloy, a new commercial aircraft, etc. Even where the fatigue program has more research orientation or is directed toward establishing structural design methodology, the time and cost constraints still loom important. This is because other managers than, say, research managers have established the timing and funding of a developmental effort, only part of which applies to the fatigue researcher or engineer.

Early recognition of these constraints then permits the research worker or engineer to concentrate on establishing a sound experiment containing the five requisites cited by Natrella [1].[1]

1. Objectives that are clearly defined and limited in extent.
2. An experiment that provides a measure of the effect of the variables of interest not obscured by the uncontrolled variables.
3. An experiment that is reasonably free from bias.
4. An experiment that provides a measure of experimental error or precision.
5. Precision that is sufficient to answer the questions posed by the stated objectives.

2.2.3 Cost Estimation

Although each research and development organization has its own methods of collecting and accounting for the cost of research and testing, some guidelines can be provided of the cost elements for fatigue programs. The importance of some of the elements varies, depending upon whether the program is a basic materials program or a large-scale structural test.

1. Program supervision and engineering.
2. Materials and supplies[2].

[1] The italic numbers in brackets refer to the list of references appended to each chapter.
[2] In a structural or component test, strain gages, stress coat, etc., may be used: these are supplies.

3. Specimen fabrication.
4. Fixture design, fabrication, and checkout.
5. Instrumentation design, assembly, and checkout.
6. Specimen set-up time.
7. Technician time for monitoring tests, making measurements, recording data, and examining failed specimens.
8. Equipment charges for maintenance and depreciation.
9. Data analysis and report preparation.

2.3 Test Program Design

Fatigue programs, even when modest in scope, are expensive and time consuming. It is, therefore, highly desirable that such programs yield the maximum amount of unambiguous information with a minimum investment of time and cost. Statistical design and analysis of fatigue experiments usually will give the investigator the "most for his money" both in the amount of usable information and in the ability to quantify the confidence in his conclusions.

Some programs involving materials and structural elements are generally designed to provide information on one (or a few) facets of an engineering problem (for example, the effect of heat-treatment process on the fatigue behavior of an alloy or the effect of hole-coldworking procedures on the behavior of structural joints). Such programs are planned in such a manner that load and environmental variables (or damage-inducing agents) are maintained constant except the factor under consideration. This factor, then, is systematically varied over some limited or extensive range of interest.

Other programs may not lend themselves to a single-variable approach, particularly those that may be associated with service simulation in which a variety of damage-inducing agents, and a variety of loads and environments may vary with time in some complex manner. An example of the type of program where a single-variable approach may not be completely pertinent is the structural joint problem previously cited. In structural joints, hole-coldworking procedure is only one variable that affects joint fatigue behavior. Other factors include the fastener, its configuration and material, the clamping force in the fastener, the joint material, the joint design, the nature of the interface, etc. A limited program with one joint design, one fastener and clamping force, one material, etc., and many hole-preparation techniques may provide such a limited amount of information that erroneous conclusions could be drawn. On the other hand, to evaluate all of the variables involved in a full-blown test matrix could be well beyond the realm of time and cost.

In recognition of these complexities in planning experimental programs (even single-variable programs), considerable attention has been given to the development of experimental design techniques which are aimed at providing usable information in such a way that one can quantify the confidence in conclusions arising from the research. It is not the intent in this handbook to describe in detail the complex area of experimental design. Instead, a brief background of some features leading to sound experimental design is provided with the implied understanding that readers will refer to other references on experimental design, such as Refs *1-11.*

2.3.1 Requirements of a Sound Experiment

In the section on General Planning, one subsection contained a list of the five requisites to consider in planning a sound experiment. These requisites are related to the procedure of experimental design and some of them are amplified to some extent in this subsection.

Clearly Defined Objectives—This requisite has been described adequately in the General Planning section and is not further treated here, except to say that a clear statement of objectives and scope implies that the investigator has some positive understanding of what hypothesis is being tested (or alternates), or what data and analysis is required to establish narrow or broad empirical rules of behavior.

Clear Measurement of the Effect of Program Variables—The objective of an investigation is to be able to measure the effects of the variables of interest on fatigue behavior and to separate these effects from those associated with uncontrolled variables and experimental error. The variables of interest are the factors that are aystematically varied in the program. In the planning operation, levels of the factors to be evaluated are established. These levels may be qualitative (for example, in hole preparation, one might evaluate drilling, reaming, honing, and bearingizing as a coldworking procedure) or quantitative (for example, several discrete levels of oxygen content for a given titanium alloy). For qualitative variables, one must consider defining the process. For quantitative variables, one is concerned with establishing either fixed values or random values within a practical range with some consideration of accuracy in specifying the levels.

Uncontrolled variables can include environmental effects for long-time programs, time, sampling heterogeneity with regard to materials, multiple-test machine use, etc. Program planning requires detailed consideration of such factors.

Freedom from Bias—Systematic error or bias can result in ambiguous results and the risk of arriving at invalid conclusions. It is the investigator at the planning stage who can minimize bias and assure that conclusions are valid, through the use of randomization and local control.

Bias can be introduced into a program when specimens, for example, are obtained from two different plates or bars of a given material; or where specimen fabrication is done by more than one machinist; or where, to compress testing time, several fatigue machines are used, etc. In the experimental design, the investigator should be aware that these factors have to be accounted for to minimize bias. At his disposal are (1) the local control procedures such as blocking, nesting, or analysis of covariance, and (2) randomization which ensures that if systematic errors are present, all tests will be biased equally, but that differences due to the controlled variables will be free of bias.

Experimental Error—A sound experiment should contain an internal estimate of the precision or experimental error inherent in the combination of experimental techniques, instrumentation, and testing machine precision of which the experiment is comprised. This experimental error is used in the analysis of the data to assess the statistical significance of the effects of the controlled variables. In approaching this part of the experimental design, the investigator has at his disposal replication to provide the measure of precision.

Precision—The precision in a sound experimental design should be adequate to detect the effects of the controled variables with an acceptable risk of incorrect conclusions. Increasing replication improves the precision and equal replication for each treatment (combinations of levels of controlled factors or variables) maximizes the precision of estimates of effects. As this phase of planning is carried out by the investigator, it will become evident that increased precision increases the cost of the experiment. Thus, he has to measure and evaluate both cost and consequence of incorrect conclusions in arriving at his plan. He should keep in mind, however, that experimental precision can be increased by (1) refinement of techniques and instrumentation, (2) selection of the appropriate test plan, and (3) introduction of local control.

The thought regarding selection of an appropriate test plan brings one to a more practical consideration in the process of developing a sound program. In a real sense, the investigator will probably draw up several candidate experimental designs which then are compared and evaluated in light of the constraints of time and cost. Each of the plans will be evaluated with regard to experimental error, adequacy to detect differences within the acceptable risk of wrong conclusions, ability to separate controlled and uncontrolled factors, etc. There are prediction-analysis tools available to the investigator as described in Refs *8* and *11-15* that he can use to predict the precision of the response obtained from such candidate plans so that he can arrive at the most efficient design of the experiment.

2.3.2 Specimen Considerations

In view of the diverse objectives that have been the basis for research in fatigue or materials, there has been an almost unlimited variety of specimens employed. Chapter 6 in this manual describes some features in the design and fabrication of specimens for materials evaluations. In the planning stage, some thought has to be given by the investigator to specimen design and how it will be influenced by the program and the equipment available. The discussion in Chapter 6 should provide some guidance; however, recommended practices such as ASTM Recommended Practice for Constant Amplitude Axial Fatigue Tests of Metallic Materials (E 466-72 T) provide general guidance for materials type specimens.

The design of more complex specimens, simulating structural elements and built-up structures, frequently is related to a particular region in a structure. In these cases, the specimen design, the materials, and fabrication processes utilized are dictated by the structure. Where a program is directed at verifying a design or developing allowable fatigue stresses to use in design, it is important that material, heat treatment, fabrication procedures, and design details be very close to that experienced by the structure or element.

For the very complex structure, costly to build and test, it is frequently necessary to test other than the complete structure. This sectioning out of a part of the structure provides the fatigue engineer with a possible technical constraint on the resulting data. This constraint is related to the stress analysis of the structure and element and the realistic simulation of the stresses in the element. It is not sufficient to know the configuration of stresses in the element when it is sound. One must also know how the stresses change as the element sustains damage. For example, fatigue damage in a nonredundant element builds up at a very fast rate compared with a redundant element where one might encounter crack arrest due to load relief to adjacent elements in the structure. The assumed boundary conditions in analysis are not always correct in practice and, hence, test validity can often be questionable for this reason.

Once the stress or strain history has been established, the test planner can either consider idealized loadings or attempt to simulate the load history involved, which brings up another technical constraint which the investigator must assess.

If the fatigue test involves more than one stress level, it will be necessary to establish several factors affecting the development of the load spectrum. In nearly every case with variable loads, there is a degree of uncertainty in the application of these loads. While a constant-amplitude sinewave is deterministic and does not present the problems of "programmed-loading" situations, the accumulation of fatigue damage under such an idealization is unique to that loading history.

By examining the statistical aspects of variable amplitude situations, one can arrive at a design load spectrum which will encompass all the excursions in loading in such a manner as to yield a conservative minimum fatigue life for the element. Even random loadings can be statistically represented by deterministic design values for this purpose, if carefully programmed, although a review of the literature will reveal that factors such as load sequence, interaction between load levels, and the shape of the loading cycle can greatly alter the fatigue life.

For many elements, a "duty cycle" can be developed for a programmed fatigue test. This is simply a sequence of loading considered typical for the use of the material or structure (for example, a flight-by flight load profile simulating an actual single-flight mission for an aircraft). This duty cycle then is applied repeatedly to the test piece to determine its endurance. However, even in this case, the assumed "duty cycle" may not completely simulate actual service; hence an attempt to provide such a spectrum to yield a conservative minumum fatigue life is made.

2.4 Conduct of a Program

The sequence of events in a fatigue program leading up to the data analysis and reporting is referred to as the test procedure. Subsection 2.4.1 describes a typical sequence. Subsection 2.4.2 describes certain precautions to be considered in carrying out the procedure. It is assumed that the fatigue experiment has been designed (earlier sections of this chapter), the equipment selected (Chapters 3 and 4), verified (Chapter 7), and the specimen designed (Chapter 6).

2.4.1 Test Procedure

Step 1—Carry out all the specimen preparation procedures. For a materials program, this would include:

(*a*) cut specimens from the parent material (for example, bar, plate, etc.), number them,[3] and record their location in the parent material;
(*b*) rough-machine the specimens;
(*c*) carry out final heat-treatment operations, if necessary;
(*d*) finish-machine the specimens; and
(*e*) polish, if required.

Step 2—Check calibrations (Chapter 7). Ensure that the machine has been verified (in the loading range desired) recently, and that there have been no unusual problems with the machine since the last verification.

Step 3—Set up the data log. The data log should contain all the information required for a reader who did not witness the test so that the test can be repeated, if necessary.

Step 4—Machine reset and warm-up. Many types of fatigue test systems require a period of time to stabilize prior to their use.

Step 5—Mount the test piece in the machine (see Subsection 2.4.2).

---

[3] It is assumed that in program planning the experimental design has included randomization, and that the specimen numbering procedure is a part of the plan.

Step 6—Initialize the test. In this step, the counters or timers are set to zero or their value noted. The programmers are initialized (for example, reset) and the readout devices set.

Step 7—Set the fail-safe devices. In this step, activate (if possible) all elements designed to protect the test from undesirable loads or strains.

Step 8—Start the test (see Subsection 2.4.2).

Step 9—Check the running test (see Subsection 2.4.2).

Step 10—Establish the failure criterion. This step is anticipated earlier, but usually occurs at this chronological point. Whatever definition of failure has been agreed upon, for example, excessive strain, load drop-off, etc., the device measuring this quantity is now connected into the test system so that the attainment of the critical value of the parameter causes the test system to stop.

This criterion may not even be a failure criterion; for example, it may be required merely to fatigue load a specimen for a predetermined length of time or for a predetermined number of cycles.

The criterion may also be one which must be applied manually. For example, the test engineer may be instructed to stop the test at the first visual indication of fatigue damage.

Whatever criterion is used in a test program, it must be explicitly noted and consistently applied.

Step 11—Stop the test (see Subsection 2.4.2).

Step 12—Remove the specimen (see Subsection 2.4.2).

Step 13—Complete the log sheet. All pertinent data for the test should be written down before the machine is reset. The specimen should also be examined carefully and all pertinent details of failure noted. If examination of the specimen is postponed, or if it is desired to preserve the specimen for later examination, methods to combat corrosion or any other time-dependent effect must be used.

One final point with regard to test procedure: be alert to the possibility of providing seemingly redundant information. It is better to have more information on a test log than seems necessary. The redundancies in such a log are excellent cross-checking devices. There are many cases where an expensive fatigue test has been salvaged from a situation involving defective cycle counters by meticulous attention and recording of frequencies and starting and stopping times.

2.4.2 Test Precautions

Step 5—In attaching the specimen to the grips of the fatigue machine, one should be careful not to prestrain the specimen excessively, since large strains can influence the results. A rule of thumb is to limit such loads or strains to 25 percent of the fatigue limit.

Step 8—A given test is to be subjected to a given load or strain-time relation. During start-up, there may be undershooting or overshooting for some number of cycles which should be recorded as load or strain-time traces for inclusion in the test log.

Step 9—After the test is running, the test engineer or technician should study the behavior of the specimen to determine whether there is excessive vibration, heat buildup, or other unusual circumstances associated with the test. Such observations may be cause to interrupt the test or modify the setup.

Step 11—As with start-up, when a test is stopped without specimen failure, there may be spurious loads or strains applied to the specimen. If the fatigue test is to be followed by some other test (a fracture test, for example), the spurious loads may influence the test. Once again, load or strain-time traces during start-up and shut-down on instrumented dummy specimens of identical design will provide information for the test log.

In the case of specimen failure, it is presumed that the test engineer has given some thought to protecting personnel from injury.

Step 12—Care should be exercised in removing specimens from the fatigue machine. If they are unbroken, the care is to minimize excessive loads or strains. If they are broken, the care is to prevent damage to the fracture surface.

2.5 Presentation of Data

2.5.1 Analysis

A number of fundamental concepts utilized in designing experiments (such as, organizational structure, experimental units, blocking, treatments, randomization, replication, etc.) are valid in planning any test program whether or not the data are subsequently subjected to statistical analysis. This statement admits the existence of the powerful statistical analysis tools that an investigator can use; however, it also admits the reality that the analysis of results of many fatigue programs is done without statistics, usually employing trend lines. One other important feature of the statement, probably the most important, is that the tool termed "statistical design of experiments" is a potent mechanism in the planning of a sound experiment.

Each program has an objective and possibly several subobjectives. Each program has a plan, simple or complex in accordance with the objectives and the time and cost constraints imposed on the investigator. After the test phase of a program, the investigator then has his pool of data, which with analysis is employed to test hypotheses, intuitive ideas and concepts, or to construct behavioral models. Available to the investigator are statistical tools or more subjective trend analyses. It is important to understand that it is not at this point in the program that one decides to use statistical analysis or not. That decision is made during the design of the experiment, when one is measuring the objectives, the risk of providing incorrect answers, the program size, and the time and cost constraints, Only at that point can the experiment be formulated to best utilize powerful statistical analysis tools.

2.5.2 Reporting

The aim of this subsection is not to describe a program report. The concern of this brief section is with the competent reporting of the experiment and the data obtained therefrom. Since fatigue data never seem to disappear, it becomes important to understand what is meant by competent reporting. Simply, competent reporting embodies reporting the following information so that some future fatigue engineer can decide whether the data are useful to his purpose.

1. Material, product form, and special process purpose.
2. Mechanical properties and microstructure of the material in the fatigue specimen.
3. Specimen design.
4. Steps in specimen preparation.
5. Design of the program.
6. Fatigue equipment description and test procedures.
7. Ambient condition of temperature and humidity during tests, including an identification of purposefully corrosive environments.
8. Failure criterion, which may or may not be physical separation.
9. Post-test examination of specimens.
10. Tabular presentation of the stress-lifetime data or crack length-cycles data for fatigue-crack propagation.

Each of these features of the data is described in some detail in ASTM E 466-72 T. Although this practice is for constant-amplitude fatigue tests, essentially the same information is needed for variable load amplitude testing. A critical addition, however, is a sufficient description of the fatigue spectrum.

2.6 Multilaboratory Test Programs

This concluding section is concerned with two types of programs in which several laboratories have a part. In one of these, the emphasis is on data generation; in the other, technique and test method development.

2.6.1 Multilaboratory Data Generation

The characterization of the fatigue behavior of a material, in order to provide design data, can be accomplished by a formal or informal arrangement among several organizations. In a formal arrangement, there may be a steering group that represents each organization and provides the program planning function, allocates specific tasks to each organization, monitors test procedures for reasonable uniformity, collects all the data generated and serves in the analysis function. In such an arrangement, the degree of control may be sufficient to permit a statistically designed experiment.

In an informal arrangement, there may be no formal planning, other than agreement to evaluate a given material at a given heat treatment level in fatigue and then to pool the data. Each participant then is free to obtain his test material, determine heat treatment procedures and other processing, configure specimens, conduct tests, and report results. The informality can provide problems in analysis since there may be slight differences among companies in the individual material procurement specifications, there may be different processing and heat treatment paths utilized, specimen details, types and severity of notches may vary widely (or not at all), and test procedures and laboratory environments also may be different. One can expect that consolidation of such data can be difficult, since each data collection would have to be tested to determine how reasonable is a decision to pool data. This is the same problem that exists when the fatigue engineer searches out existing data on a given material, with the objective of consolidating it to provide design allowables.

There is an obvious agreement that a formal multilaboratory data generation program will be a sounder way to characterize a material's fatigue behavior following some organizational features of the next subsection. It is also the approach that is the most difficult to organize.

2.6.2 Interlaboratory Test Programs [16]

The general objective of interlaboratory test programs is to study or to measure or both the variability in fatigue data, usually associated with a test method development. The interlaboratory study is designed to evaluate the precision of a method (or variations of a method) within a laboratory or between several laboratories. Another objective is to discover previously unidentified sources of variations in test results. A control committee is required to plan, control, and analyze the experiment subject to the following rules.

1. A central group (established by the committee) should select, prepare, and distribute, in a completely random manner, the specimens to participating laboratories.
2. Each participating laboratory must be skilled and familiar with the test method to be studied.
3. Laboratories should run the tests in random order.
4. Each laboratory should be supplied with additional specimens to be

used in case of loss or damage to any specimens. All laboratories should test an identical number of specimens.

5. Each laboratory should be *instructed* to adhere *strictly* to prescribed procedures of measurement. They should be encouraged to submit observations and remarks that might prove helpful in the interpretation of the data.

6. Each laboratory should be *instructed* to report their results *as obtained*, preferably on a standardized form.

7. All computations *must* be done by a central group of which at least one member is thoroughly familiar with the statistical techniques of experiment design and analysis [17].

In summary, the key words are *Plan, Control, Analysis,* and *Randomization.*

FIG. 1—*An example of Murphy's Law as applied to a fatigue crack propagation test.*

2.7 Final Remarks

Looking into the future, one can visualize an extension of the use of computers into the area of test planning. For example, the test engineer would enter into a "conversation" with a computer preloaded with a "logic-tree" so that the correct fatigue test can be arrived at by a succession of branching operations based on the engineer's replies to questions asked (for example, type of specimen, ranges of test parameters, etc.). By coupling such a question-answer program with a data bank, the engineer can even avoid repeating the test if the data has already been generated.

Of course, sometimes even with the best planning in the world, one ends up with results as shown in Fig. 1.

References

[1] Natrella, M. G., *Experimental Statistics, NBS Handbook 91,* U.S. Government Printing Office, Washington, D.C. 1963.

[2] Hald, A., *Statistical Theory with Engineering Applications,* Wiley, New York, 1952.

[3] Wilson, E. B., Jr., *An Introduction to Scientific Research,* McGraw-Hill Book Co., New York, 1952.

[4] Brownlee, K. A., *Industrial Experimentation,* Chemical Rubber Publishing Co., New York, 1953.

[5] Cox, D. R., *Planning of Experiments,* Wiley, New York, 1958.

[6] Crow, E. L., Davis, F. A., and Maxfield, M. W., *Statistics Manual,* Dover Publications, New York, 1960.

[7] Finney, D. J., *An Introduction to the Theory of Experimental Design,* The University of Chicago Press, Chicago, 1960.

[8] Schenck, H., Jr., *Theories of Engineering Experimentation,* McGraw-Hill Book Co., New York, 1961.

[9] Davies, O. L., Ed., *Design and Analysis of Industrial Experiments,* 2nd ed., Oliver and Boyd, London, 1963.

[10] Hicks, C. R., *Fundamental Concepts in the Design of Experiments,* Holt, Rinehart and Winston, Inc., New York, 1964.

[11] Chatfield, C., *Statistics for Technology,* Penguin Books, Baltimore, 1970.

[12] Parratt, L. G., *Probability and Experimental Errors in Science,* Wiley, New York, 1961.

[13] Mandel, J., *The Statistical Analysis of Experimental Data,* Interscience Publishers, New York, 1964.

[14] Hahn, G. J. and Shapior, S. S., *Statistical Models in Engineering,* Wiley, New York, 1967.

[15] Wolberg, J. R., *Prediction Analysis,* D. Van Nostrand Co., New York, 1967.

[16] *Manual for Conducting an Interlaboratory Study of a Test Method, ASTM STP 335,* American Society for Testing and Materials, 1963.

[17] Youden, W. J., *Statistical Techniques for Collaborative Tests,* AOAC, 1967.

Chapter 3—Basic Elements of a Fatigue Test System

3.1 Introduction

All fatigue test systems, regardless of complexity, consist of the same basic elements. In simple systems, these elements are extremely rudimentary. On the other hand, sophisticated systems require highly complex elements. A test system loads the specimen through the load train, commands and programs the test through controls, monitors the test through sensors, and communicates with the investigator by means of read-out devices. The essential features of these elements are described in this chapter.

3.2 The Load Train

The load train consists of a frame, grips, specimen, and drive (or loading) system.

In fatigue tests of materials and small components, a load frame is required for reacting forces applied to the specimen by the drive system, and to support the specimen and sensors associated with the specific test. Provisions are made to assure convenience in mounting the specimen and auxiliary equipment such as environmental chambers. A high degree of accessibility in the specimen test area is most desirable.

The load frame is any suitable mechanical structure which can react the force (axial load, moment, or torque) applied to the specimen. The structural stiffness (or spring rate) of the frame effects the cycling frequency of load application. The stiffer the frame, the higher the cyclic frequency allowed in the test. Hence, one of the factors to consider when selecting a test frame is the compromise between capability and stiffness, and actual usage requirements.

In a closed-loop system, especially, the load frame is part of the feedback loop; and as such, must remain a passive element. If, for example, the loading of the specimen created resonance in the frame, the test would be disrupted with possible damage to the specimen. Several examples of load frames are shown and described in the next few paragraphs.

The frame in Fig. 2 is typical of those designed specifically for fatigue use, but may also be used for general purpose testing. It has a separable upper crosshead attached to the table by a pattern of bolts. Note that the stressed length of the frame is minimized. Also, the base is made very

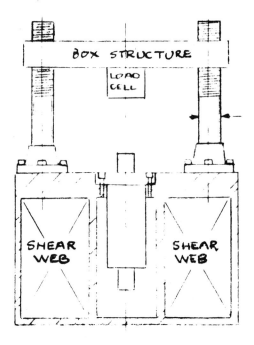

FIG. 2—*Frame designed specifically for fatigue use.*

rigid by the incorporation of mulitple shear webs, which permit little deflection either vertically or laterally.

The upper crosshead is formed as a rigid closed box structure, which provides good stiffness, minimum weight and a resulting high resonant frequency. The entire frame is constructed such that all connections are pretensioned above the frame rating, which minimizes fatigue effects.

Figure 3 is a typical frame for static and low cycle fatigue testing. Note again, that the stressed length is minimized from the load cell to the actuator. The extensions of the columns below the platen are preloaded in excess of the force rating of the frame so that they are effectively removed from the force loop. Large tubes are used to react the preload forces, and also to provide good transverse stiffness, for general purpose usage.

All the major frame connections are pretensioned above the frame rating and so are not subjected to fatigue or shifting under load.

The base casting is only used to support the frame on the floor and does not, in itself, react any load.

The frame in Fig. 4 is typical of those in use for static testing and low cycle fatigue work. In this case, the effective force loop is a function of the crosshead position. However, since the crosshead slides on the rods, the overall stiffness must be expressed, at least partially, as a function of the overall frame dimensions.

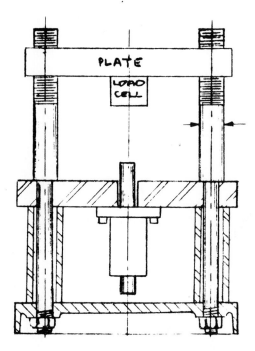

FIG. 3—*A typical frame for static and low cycle fatigue testing.*

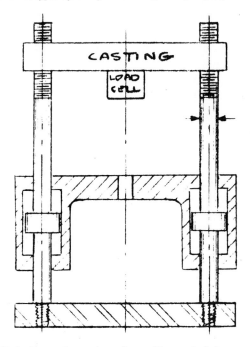

FIG. 4—*Frame for static testing and low cycle fatigue work.*

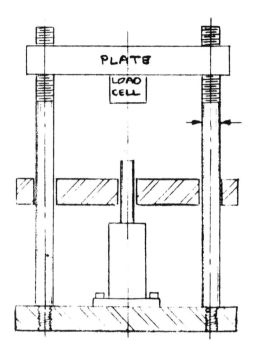

FIG. 5—*Frame for static testing and low cycle fatigue work.*

The forcing pistons are ordinarily connected in parallel, so that an equal force is generated in each ram. Thus, if an eccentric load is imposed, it causes a force couple which must be reacted by the overall frame structure. Variations in friction in the two pistons can cause a significant misalignment of the overall framework, from the resulting imbalance of forces.

The frame in Fig. 5 is also typical of the types used for static testing and low cycle fatigue work. The lower platen may either be coupled to the actuator so that it moves up and down with the actuator piston, or decoupled from the actuator so that it rests on stops attached to the base.

In this case, the stressed length is quite long. The side stiffness of the frame, being approximately proportional to the cube of the column length, is substantially less than the first two frames with their shorter effective column length. The relative stiffness is also less because smaller diameter columns are employed for an equivalent frame force rating. It will also be noted, that side loads on the actuator must be reacted over its entire length.

Choosing a relatively high load capability is often desirable for fatigue machines because of the accompanying improvement in stiffness. However, the cost of load frames makes too great a disparity between size and usage requirements unwise.

Many frames operate in fatigue at a maximum of 67 percent of their static rating. However, in actual practice the most frequently used range is probably 25 to 50 percent of the static rating.

In summary, the basic principles of load frame selection are:

(*a*) capacity (loading, space),
(*b*) rigidity,
(*c*) convenience in use, and
(*d*) alignment technique.

In the case of the last item, one finds two extremes. The frame is either completely adjustable for alignment, and therefore must be set and checked, or it is essentially impossible to realign, and one must be content with establishing the frame's inherent alignment characteristics.

The drive system used in a given fatigue testing machine is usually the most distinguishing feature, and typical drive systems are therefore discussed in detail in Chapter 4. The various types of grips and aspects of the gripping of fatigue are closly associated with the form of the specimen, and are dealt with in Chapter 6.

3.3 Power Supply

There are many types of power supplies for fatigue test systems, but the great majority of them are based on electricity. Electric motors may act directly on the specimen through cams, levers or rotating grips. Alternatively, electricity may be used to generate power through a second system, for example, electrohydraulic or electromagnetic.

3.4 Controls

The purpose of the controls is to continuously command the test system to follow a previously programmed test parameter (load, moment, torque, deflection, strain, etc.) of either constant or variable amplitude. In general, control includes: (1) some means of initiating the test, (2) some means of adjusting or maintaining the test parameters or both during the test in response to information supplied by the monitoring elements, and (3) some means of terminating the test upon achievement of some status (for example, specimen failure, exceedance of a predetermined number of cycles, etc.) or in reaction to a malfunction through a signal from safety cut-offs or fail-safe devices. Control may be either manual, automatic, or a combination of both.

3.4.1 Programming

For many simple constant-amplitude fatigue test systems, programming consists of initiating and maintaining a simple harmonic motion in the drive system, for example, an electric motor-driven eccentric weight or hydraulic pulsator. In the more complex test systems, electronic programmers generate an electrical signal that varies with time in the identical way that the controlled parameter is required to vary with time. Such programmers vary the mean level, amplitude, shape of the parameter-time waveform, and frequency during the prosecution of the fatigue test. Electronic programmers include constant-amplitude function generators and arbitrary program generators such as magnetic drums, random noise generators, magnetic tape readers, and both digital and analog computers.

Constant amplitude function generators provide various cyclic waveforms (for example, sine, square, triangle, etc.) over a wide range of frequencies (Fig. 6). At present, the sine waveform is the most common form used in fatigue testing. The sine wave is well-defined and easily standardized. Interesting studies have been made, however, using the other waveforms (for example, in corrosion fatigue).

Arbitrary function generators (Fig. 7) allow the investigator to more closely simulate the variable amplitude load environment of acutal service. It must be pointed out, however, that the ability of a test system to respond satisfactorily to the output of an arbitrary function generator must be investigated before initiation of the fatigue test. For example, a "soft" (that is, low stiffness) load-specimen train may not achieve the load peaks commanded, especially at high cyclic frequencies.

In the analog programming device shown in Fig. 7, any continuous line scribed on a conductively coated polyester-film chart divides it into two electrically isolated planes. Placed on the drum, the chart is energized at its edges by contacts, producing an electrostatic voltage gradient across the chart. A non-contacting electrostatic probe scans the chart, looking for the zero potential at the scribed break. A servo, sensing the polarized gradient on either side of the break, has no trouble keeping the probe at this null while positioning an output potentiometer. Adjusting drum rotation speed provides a continuously adjustable time base for the program, and since the probe never touches the chart, it can be used and reused indefinitely.

Other types of programming, as listed earlier, will be considered in later chapters (for example, computer programming in Chapter 11).

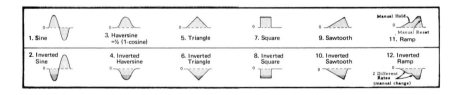

FIG. 6—*Typical waveforms used in fatigue testing.*

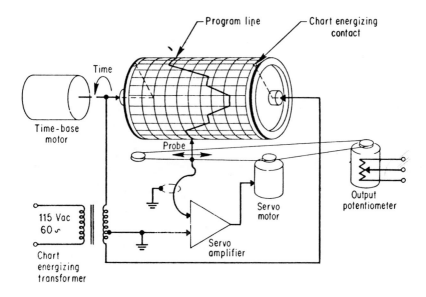

FIG. 7—*An arbitrary program drum [schematic]*.

3.4.2 Sensors

Sensors or transducers, are devices which convert a physical quantity or measurand (for example, displacement, force, etc.) into electrical pneumatic, or hydraulic output signals, Fig. 8. The general relationship between the measurand and the transducer range is shown in Fig. 9. The transducer output signal may be either (1) returned or fed back to the controls for automatic maintenance of the test program, or (2) sent to "read-out" devices for continuous communication with the investigator.

In order to provide, with a certain level of accuracy, a useful working reference to the multitude of transducers presently available to industry, it was deemed necessary that some common means for conveying and interpreting product information be developed. To this end, a series of terms and definitions were prepared (see Appendix A). These definitions were developed with full cognizance and reference to the standardization activities of the Instrument Society of America, Recommended Practices Department, American Standards Association, and International Organization for Standardization.

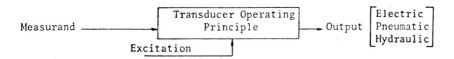

FIG. 8—*Diagram of how physical quantity is converted into output signals.*

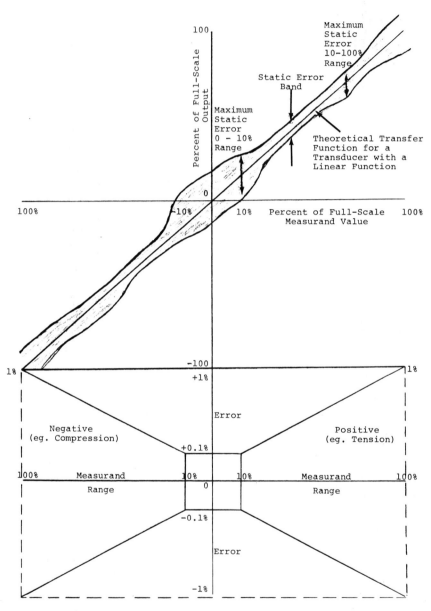

FIG. 9—*Measurand-output relation for a linear transducer, illustrating the defined characteristics and static error band representation.*

Load Cells—Forces are sensed, generally, by load cells which, with the grips are part of the load train. Load cell force transducers are available with electrical, hydraulic, or pneumatic outputs.

Load cell force transducers are generally characterized by wide magnitude range and frequency capability, as well as high accuracy and linearity. The fluid types of load cells are commonly utilized with pressure gages or recorders for local readout, and although the signal can be used directly or converted to electrical form for system applications, these devices will not be covered in this review.

Electric load cells, Fig. 10, typically contain an elastic member such as a metal column or beam, which deforms under applied force. The deformation is transmitted to a variable impedance electrical element, such as a strain gage or linear variable differential transformer (LVDT), which is used in a measuring circuit to produce an output signal. The gages are electrically connected to form a balanced Wheatstone bridge. Excitation voltage is applied across two opposite corners of the bridge. Force applied to the cell unbalances the bridge by changing the resistance of the gages and produces an output voltage. The output voltage is used as a feedback voltage in load control systems. Its polarity is positive when the applied force is tensile and negative when the force is compressive (Fig. 11).

Load cells may be obtained to measure tension, compression, or both, and to detect forces along one or several axes. Specially designed package

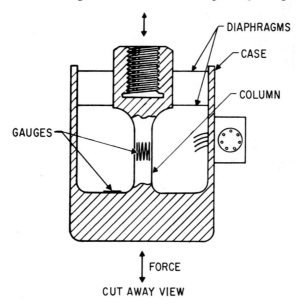

FIG. 10—*A schematic diagram of a load cell.*

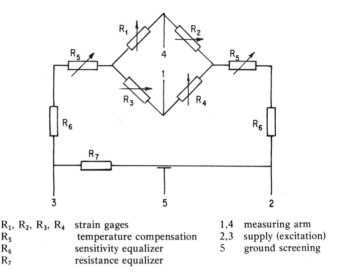

R_1, R_2, R_3, R_4	strain gages	1,4	measuring arm
R_5	temperature compensation	2,3	supply (excitation)
R_6	sensitivity equalizer	5	ground screening
R_7	resistance equalizer		

FIG. 11—*Schematic diagram of a typical load cell bridge circuit.*

configurations are also used, such as load-sensing bolts and weighing platforms, for a variety of applications.

Industrial load cells can be obtained with accuracies to 0.1 percent and linearities to 0.5 percent. Units included in this review have capabilities ranging from 0 to 2000 through 0 to 3000 tons. Other factors to be considered with load cells include input and output impedance, temperature limits, frequency response, sensitivity, and need for excitation.

Accessories such as digital indicators, printers, and recorders are available, as are complex systems for dead-weight pressure testing, weighing stations, and cranes or hoists. Most manufacturers carry an assortment of fittings, connectors, base plates, and test stands. Also, some companies supply certificates of calibration.

Linear Variable Differential Transformers [LVDT]—The LVDT is an electromechanical device which provides an output voltage proportional to the displacement of a movable core. It consists of a transformer with a primary and two secondaries, wound to a common cylindrical form and a core which is oriented axially within the hollow body of the transformer. The construction of the transformer and the connection of the secondaries (series opposition) is such that if the core is placed in a position which induces equal emf's (electromotive forces) in the two secondaries, the net output voltage will be zero (the core is said to be at electrical null). If, however, the core is displaced towards one end of the unit, mutual inductance increases between the primary and one secondary while decreasing between the primary and the other secondary—the output

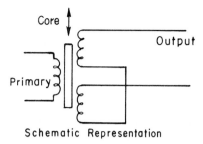

Schematic Representation

FIG. 12—*Linear variable differential transformer [LVDT].*

emf's of the two secondaries are no longer equal and a net output voltage results (Fig. 12).

Strain Gage Extensometers—Deformations and displacements may be sensed by electro-mechanical transducers such as strain-gage extensometers and linear variable differential transformers (LVDT). The strain-gage extensometer is identical, in principle, to the electrical load cell in that it converts an elastic deformation of an internal member to an electrical output signal.

Hydraulic Pressure Transducers—The test signal is transmitted to a variable impedance electrical device (for example, electric resistance strain gages, linear variable differential transformers, etc.) and then converted to an electrical output signal which is sent to recorders or as feedback or both, to the controls. Another common force transducer is the hydraulic load cell which transmits changes in force as changes in hydraulic pressure to pressure gages (for example, Bourdon tubes) for read-out. It is also common to convert this hydraulic pressure signal to an electrical signal for feedback to the controls. Some hydraulic drive systems (Chapter 4) also tap the hydraulic fluid pressure in the force generator (for example, actuator) and transmit this to pressure gages for read-out and control feedback.

3.4.3 Transducer Conditioners

The outputs of the load cell and displacement gage(s) are fed into appropriate recording systems. For static test in which only load and one displacement gage output are measured, the two outputs are fed into an X-Y recorder. For higher rate tests, these two outputs are fed into an oscilloscope and their display on the oscilloscope screen is photographed. When several transducer outputs are required to be recorded for either static or high rate tests, they are fed into the magnetic tape recorder, then subsequently played back in any desired combination on the X-Y recorder. The X-Y plot may be load versus strain, load versus displacement, etc.

Each transducer is calibrated with a transducer conditioner for an output accurate within specified limits. Load cells are normally accurate to within 0.1 percent of range or 1 percent of reading, whichever is greater, but always within 0.5 percent of range. Stroke transducers are normally accurate to 1 percent of range. Inaccuracy of the readout instrument adds to the error. Instruments for measurement of static reading can yield accuracies to 0.02 percent.

3.5 Readout Devices

One of the functions of the sensor or transducer is to provide an output signal, which is transmitted to a readout device for communication with the investigator. In some cases, visual inspection of the specimen at the conclusion of the test is sufficient to give the required information; it fractured after n cycles or remained unbroken after N cycles. A cycle counter for readout purposes is present in the most rudimentary of test systems.

More frequently, however, it is necessary to continuously sense or monitor the state of the specimen (and test system) during the prosecution of the test. For this purpose, a suitable combination of both transducers or sensors and readout devices is required for communication.

Most systems include a variety of readout equipment to facilitate the monitoring of test parameters and the recording of pertinent data. Oscilloscopes, digital readout equipment, hydraulic pressure gages, etc., will present the instantaneous state of the test and enable the investigator to ensure that the correct levels of command are being maintained. X-Y and stripchart recorders, oscillographs, and magnetic tape recorders will provide permanent records of the test parameters of importance to the investigator. However, a controlling factor is normally the frequency response of a particular type of recorder which depends upon its principle of operation, that is, ink or heat pen, light beam, etc. Another consideration in the selection of a suitable recorder is the number of parameters that are required to be sensed simultaneously. For example, an X-Y recorder can follow two parameters, whereas a multi-channel oscillograph or magnetic tape can follow many outputs simultaneously.

3.5.1 Oscilloscopes

For short duration tests, the stress-strain curve is often displayed on the oscilloscope screen and photographed. The transducer outputs recorded during the conventional fatigue tests are those from the load cell and the strain gage extensometer. Oscilloscopes are, perhaps, the most widely used dynamic readout for continuous monitoring of fatigue tests.

An amplitude measurement device is often used with the oscilloscope. This device will chop a fatigue signal to permit comparison of the peak and trough values with a reference voltage (any precise voltage between, say ±10 V). This permits the adjusting of the fatigue load maxima and minima to precise values.

3.5.2 Recorders

For tests which require the recording of more than two parameters, a magnetic tape recorder can be used. Some of these have 14 channels, and tape speeds ranging from 1-7/8 in. per s to 60 in. per s.

The recording devices most frequently used in fatigue systems are X-Y or X-Y-Y recorders which enable curves of one or two variables to be plotted against another, or against time. They are used principally in low-speed systems for plotting curves of load versus strain, etc. They have a full-scale response of approximately 1 s, that is, they can traverse the full width of the chart in 1 s (the slewing speed).

A strip chart recorder or X-Y plotter is normally accurate to 0.2 percent at low speeds. Strip chart recorders and oscillographs can be used in fatigue testing systems to record functions having frequencies up to 1000 Hz, depending on the principle of operation (for example, ink, light beam, etc.). A recorder input selector panel is usually included as an input device to a recorder.

3.6 Safety Cut-Offs

The types of available fail-safe and cut-off devices are many and varied as are their functions. Some devices terminate the test upon specimen failure or upon achievement of a predetermined number of cycles or test running time. Specimen failure may be fracture, excessive deformation, or crack length of an arbitrary, but fixed, size. Other devices sense changes in measured parameters that cannot be corrected by the control system and, having decided that the test is no longer in control, terminate the test. Still other devices detect conditions unsafe for the operating personnel, test system, or specimen (for example, low fluid levels in hydraulic systems, overtemperatures, etc.) and terminate the test or even prevent test initiation. Safety cut-offs and fail-safe devices include electro-mechanical limit switches as well as electronic operational amplifiers.

There are a number of simple mechanical switches which are used to serve as cut-off switches when physically depressed by, for example, the excursions of a (constant-load amplitude) cracking member.

Additionally, closed-loop control for testing brings with it the possibility of loop divergence, and other erratic behavior common to the malfunction of any servo system. This problem is especially significant in fatigue systems using hydraulic power, since such systems have the capability not only to apply very large forces, but to do so at the high speed associated with the frequency response needed for fast fatigue cycling. These considerations, combined with the generally high cost of the larger fatigue specimens, make such test "wipe outs" very serious matters.

Closed-loop control implies that the machine is thinking for the operator at all times during the test. The test system must be told what to do before that portion of the test begins. If something is left out in the loop, it is often too late to do anything about it once the test commences. It is not unusual to see an operator with one hand on the "panic" button while the other hand presses the start button!

Among the various things which can go wrong are:

(*a*) a defective unit in the control loop,

(*b*) an outside influence such as a general power cut-off or transient,

(*c*) improper control settings (this possibility is minimized by rigid adherence to check lists), and

(*d*) unforeseen occurrences—extensometer slippage, etc.

Many operators of closed-loop equipment will frequently interject a dummy specimen stronger than necessary (or more flexible, etc.) to have the assurance of a "dry run." A dry run checkout panel similar to those used in space flight operations, which will permit the operator to view the "go" status of each element in the loop before he carries out the test, is highly desirable.

The more traditional method of defeating the consequences of a malfunction is through the use of fail-safe devices, which fall into three categories:

(*a*) hydraulic devices,

(*b*) mechanical devices, and

(*c*) electronic devices.

Fail-safe logic is especially important in the fatigue testing of large structures. A more detailed discussion of the problem will be found in Chapter 10.

3.7 Devices to Alter the Mode of Loading

In many cases, the mode of loading can be altered by placing intermediate fixtures between the jaws of what is basically an axial-load machine. The following paragraphs provide some examples of this approach.

Transverse Testing Attachments for Three-Point Loading (Fig. 13)

A transverse testing arrangement allows the operator to conduct tests on flat bars, welded joints, and constructional parts. In addition to its use for

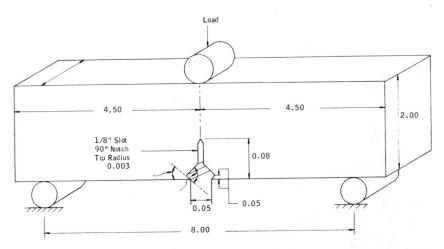

FIG. 13—*Schematic example of a three-point transverse loading arrangement for bend tests.*

testing standard specimens, the transverse beam provides valuable facilities as a gripping table for tests on constructional parts and machinery
elements, such as, for instance, shafts held as a cantilever for transverse
or simultaneous transverse and torsion tests, for testing ball bearings, or
even for testing complete gear units. The necessary holders can easily be
made by users to suit their special requirements. The transverse beam is
constructed as a support of constant strength. The outer supports are
carried in a T-slot and can be displaced steplessly to any desired distance
apart. This slot can also be used for fixing any other testing device. The
middle support has the same width as the two end supports. The knives
are made of hardened steel. For testing structural parts and similar
objects, users can easily prepare a lower support suitable for their special
requirements.

The transverse beam, being the heavier part of the equipment, is fixed
to the upper gripping head of the machine, while the much lighter middle
support is usually attached to the lower grips. With this arrangement, the
influence of the mass of the transverse beam on the dynamometer is
excluded and an accurate load measurement is thereby ensured.

In order to make use of the available stroke as rationally as possible,
diagrams are usually supplied by machine manufacturers with the working
instructions for the transverse testing arrangement, which enable the
operator to select for bars of rectangular section and a given thickness,
the stresses, width of specimen, and the distance between end supports,
also the loads which can be reached at the maximum deformation.

Transverse Testing Attachment for Four-Point Loading

The transverse testing device shown in Fig. 14 provides for the testing of

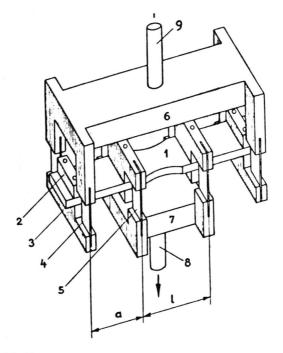

FIG. 14—*Diagram of a four-point transverse testing attachment.*

specimens, with a constant bending moment within the inner two loading pickups. The stress can be applied symmetrically (±) or with a preload, that is, unilaterally. Flat, as well as round bars, can be tested. Soldered and welded joints also can be tested in this device.

The operating principle of the arrangement is shown in Fig. 14. The specimen (1) is held by the clamps 2 and 3. These clamps are elastically connected to the crossbeams 6 and 7 by the strip pivots 4 and 5. The load is applied through the pins 8 and 9, by means of which the transverse testing arrangement is gripped in the machine in the same manner as an ordinary tensile specimen. Specimen 1, therefore, is stressed over the length (L) under the constant moment calculated as

$$M = \frac{P}{2} \cdot a$$

The distance (*a*) can be adjusted to four positions whereby the value of the maximum moments can be altered within wide limits.

Often it is desirable to use spring-rollers at the loading points, to ensure that no constraint loads are inadvertently set up in the specimen (Fig. 15).

FIG. 15—*Photo of a typical four-point bending attachment.*

Arrangement for Torsion Tests

The principle of the torsion testing attachment is shown in Fig. 16. A cylindrical specimen (3) is gripped at both ends by the flanges 4 and 5. These latter are connected elastically by the pair of strip pivots 1 and 2 to the crossbeams 6 and 7, and these latter are gripped in the test machine by means of the pins 8 and 9. With the vertical movement of the crossbeams towards each other, a pure torque is applied through the flanges 4 and 5 to the specimen (3), which can be calculated from the load and the distance apart of the strip pivots 1 and 2.

In order that the size of the specimen for a given test diameter can be kept as small as possible and yet receive a solid connection with the end flanges, rings of soft steel are shrunk on to the ends of the specimen.

These rings are then held by friction by means of a number of screws in the flanges of the torsion attachment. Wedges, cotters, or similar devices are, therefore, unnecessary.

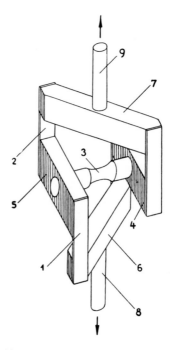

FIG. 16—*Principle of the torsion attachment.*

Chapter 4—Drive Systems for Conventional Fatigue Testing Machines

4.1 Introduction

Knowledge of the capabilities and limitations of the various types of fatigue testing systems is a prerequisite to the selection of equipment for a fatigue laboratory and in the planning and execution of meaningful and economic fatigue investigations. However, fatigue testing is unique in the area of mechanical testing in that so many varieties and types of testing devices have been developed. This chapter is intended to provide a guide to the basic principles of the operation, the capabilities, and the limitations of the more commonly used fatigue testing machines as influenced by the drive systems. Specialized machines, such as those used for rolling contact fatigue testing are also dealt with.

The four basic elements of fatigue testing systems were discussed in Chapter 3—load train, controls, sensors, and communications. The keystone of the load train, and of the entire test system, is the *drive system*. The prime function of the drive system is to receive a time-dependent signal (the program) from the controls, convert that signal to a force- or displacement-time excitation, and faithfully transfer that excitation to the specimen to be fatigue tested. However, because of the nature of the various drive systems available in current fatigue machines, there is a wide range in versatility of test systems. In this context, a high degree of versatility in a fatigue test system implies that the drive system is capable of responding not only to simple sinusoidal input signals, but also to very complex signals characteristic of or simulating actual service load or deflection histories. Therefore, the planning of a fatigue laboratory requires careful assessment of the type of research and testing that is to be carried out so that the needed capabilities of the test machines are available.

There are a number of ways to categorize fatigue test systems and then to discuss the range of available drive systems. In this chapter, it was considered that the logical approach would be to consider the drive systems for each of the three common modes of loading—axial, bending, and torsion. However, prior to getting into the specific systems, Section 4.2 contains a discussion of certain features of test systems that can be used to weigh the characteristics of particular drive systems against the requirements that a fatigue engineer believes are necessary in order to generate meaningful information.

4.2 Features of Test Systems

In addition to the mode of loading, the features of a test system that influence or are influenced by the drive system are as follows.

(a) Parameters under control.
(b) Programming capability.
(c) Control mode.
(d) Closed-loop control.
(e) Energy transfer.
(f) Energy conservation.

A test system embodies some combination of each of these features and each feature has some range of variability that makes a given test system more or less versatile. These features are discussed in this section with some attempt at explaining their limitations and advantages. It should be noted that each of the features falls within another categorization system for drive systems: (1) features that influence their reaction to the command signal [for example, (a), (b), and (c)] and (2) features that influence their reaction to their physical operating characteristics [for example, (d), (e), and (f)].

4.2.1 Parameter Under Control

There are many parameters capable of control in fatigue test systems. Three common ones are: (1) force, (2) deflection or displacement, and (3) strain at a given point on the specimen. Some drive systems are able to control only one of these parameters. Other drive systems can accommodate all three parameters and, hence, have greater versatility. Since fatigue response can vary depending upon the control parameter, as discussed in a subsequent section, this becomes an important factor in test machine and drive system assessment.

A time-varying force excitation can be produced by the centrifugal force from a rotating eccentric mass, by an electromagnetic force, by pressure-controlled hydraulic systems, or by dead weights in combination with specimen rotation (as in a rotating bending machine). It can be utilized in axial, bending, and torsion testing machines.

Time-varying deflection or displacement excitation (for example, axial elongation, bending deflection or curvature, or angular rotation) is produced with the application of reciprocating motion to a specimen. This can be achieved mechanically as with a deflecting lever in an axial load machine, a rotating eccentric attached to a bending specimen, and hydraulically through actuators.

Time-varying strain excitation can be achieved in some types of machines that are capable of monitoring the output of strain-measuring devices. Most low-cycle fatigue testing is conducted under strain control.

4.2.2 Programming Capability

In the assessment of a test system and drive system, the ability of the drive system to accommodate to a variable load or deflection history can be of particular importance to certain engineering problems. The following paragraphs describe a number of these typical input signals that can be utilized in fatigue testing.

In designing the fatigue test program, decisions must be made with regard to the required capability of the test machine to generate the signals for the test. Once these decisions have been made, the field of selection of test equipment is narrowed down considerably.

In the following categories A to G, it is generally true that the initial categories are not capable of the later category signals. For example, an F category system can simulate a C category loading, but a C category system cannot carry out F category tests.

Type A—Constant amplitude, constant frequency and, zero mean level, Fig. 17. This is the most rudimentary fatigue signal and was for many

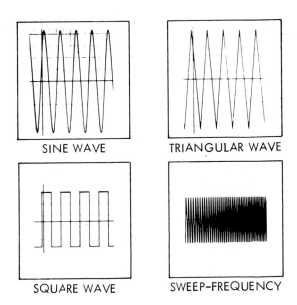

SINE WAVE   TRIANGULAR WAVE

SQUARE WAVE   SWEEP-FREQUENCY

FIG. 17—*Constant amplitude zero mean wave forms.*

years the traditional form of fatigue signal both in industry and the classroom.

Type B—Constant amplitude, constant frequency non-random with mean level, Fig. 18. These signals are of the generally used "S-N" type, where capability exists to change mean load.

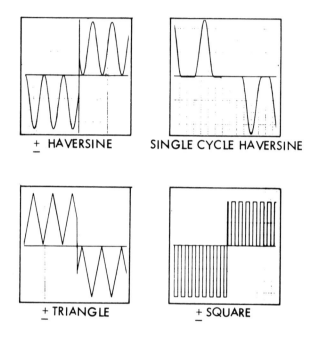

+ HAVERSINE   SINGLE CYCLE HAVERSINE

+ TRIANGLE   + SQUARE

FIG. 18—*Constant amplitude constant frequency with mean level.*

Type C—Constant amplitude with complex wave shape, Fig. 19. An example of this type of loading would be a drive system capable of combining two frequencies, with a controllable phase angle between them.

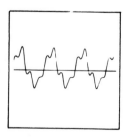

FIG. 19—*Constant amplitude with complex wave shape.*

Type D—Constant amplitude with sweep frequency capability, Fig. 17. This is simply a constant amplitude signal with capability to move from one frequency to another in a controlled "sweep," as from a low frequency to a high frequency. This type of signal, while very common in vibration testing, is little used in actual fatigue test situations, but is included for completeness.

Type E—Block constant amplitude, non-random with mean level, Fig. 20. This is typically the block constant amplitude "spectrum" loading where changes in amplitude are usually of an abrupt nature, and where the basic signal is at constant frequency within the blocks, but of lower frequency at higher amplitudes.

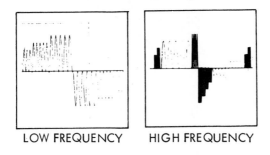

LOW FREQUENCY   HIGH FREQUENCY

FIG. 20—*Block constant amplitude with mean.*

Type F—Narrow band random or non-random without mean load or both, Fig. 21*a*. This type is typified by resonant single degree of freedom system, excited by white noise.

Type G—Narrow-band random or non-random with mean load or both, Fig. 21*b*. In this type of signal history, the frequency of operation is, as with Type F, restricted to a single narrow band. However, there is some means available for applying a steady load, and, in general, the center frequency of the dynamic component can be shifted. The dynamic

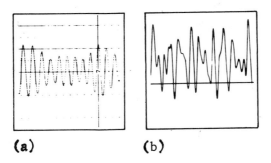

(a)   **(b)**

FIG. 21—*Narrow-bank random* (a) *without or* (b) *with mean load.*

component can be either of a non-random form (block constant amplitude at the constant frequency, or the Rayleigh type of random amplitude).

Type H—Broad-band random loading, Fig. 22. In this case, the drive system is capable of more than one frequency for the signal. One can have either zero mean load or non-zero mean load capability with this type of loading.

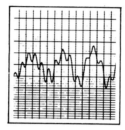

FIG. 22—*Broad-band random loading.*

Type I—Combined random and non-random without mean load capability, Fig. 23. The only difference between this signal and Type A is that there is a "forbidden region" in the frequency domain. At some low frequency, the ability to transfer energy loading to the specimen diminishes. This characteristic is inherent in what are called soft energy transfer systems.

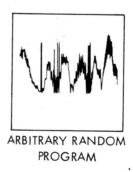

ARBITRARY RANDOM
PROGRAM

FIG. 23—*Combined random and non-random without mean load.*

In some soft energy transfer systems auxiliary devices are available to impose low frequency or mean loading. However, they are often cumbersome and cannot be altered in magnitude easily or quickly.

Type J—Combined random and non-random signal history with mean load capability, Fig. 24. The Type J signal can have components from any or all of five general load histories. (Mean load, constant amplitude, transient, filtered, continuous random process, digital random process.) The continuous random loading is capable of being either broad-band,

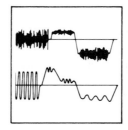

FIG. 24—*Combined random and non-random signal history with mean load.*

multiple peaked, or narrow band, depending on the frequency filtering. Systems of this type are often either computer-controlled or tape controlled. They have many applications where service simulation is of critical importance, such as in aircraft testing.

Of course, there will be some upper frequency limit for Type J systems, which must be indicated.

Many conventional drive systems can accommodate most readily only the simplest of these signals (that is, constant-amplitude excitation) and, with some difficulty, step tests that involve only a few load or deflection changes. In these systems, the load or deflection is manually set (for example, a rotating eccentric or dead-weight load) so that if a change in load or deflection is required, the test is stopped and a manual adjustment is made. For more complex load conditions, such machines are completely unsatisfactory.

Other drive systems (and test systems) are capable of instantaneous response to more complex signals, including narrow- and broad-band random signals. These drive systems can be electrohydraulic servocontrolled or electromagnetic types.

It is obvious that all fatigue testing may not require machines with the ability to respond to random input signals. However, in the selection of equipment for a laboratory or for a specific program, the capability of the equipment to produce and control the required signals has to be addressed. This is brought out with some clarity in the discussion of individual drive systems in later sections.

4.2.3. Control Mode

The context of control mode in this chapter concerns whether the system is an open-loop system or a closed-loop system. In an open-loop system, in both force and displacement-excited systems, the magnitude of the levels of the controlled excitation remains essentially the same throughout the test. However, if specimens are subjected to the same elastic stress history prior to crack initiation with either type of excitation, the cycles to specimen fracture will be different. In a displacement-excited specimen, the stiffness (or spring rate) is reduced as the fatigue crack propagates. This reduces the force amplitude of the test with a resultant reduction in crack-growth rate. On the other hand, the force amplitude in a cracked, force-excited specimen remains constant regardless of spring rate (provided that the system can accommodate the increasing displacement amplitude) and the crack-propagation rates increase with cycles. In general, for a given initial stress (or strain) state, the total number of cycles to fracture in a force-excited specimen will be significantly less than that of a displacement-excited specimen.

Therefore, even at the test program planning stage, a consideration of the relative importance of flaw propagation and flaw initiation must be made.

Non-Redundant Structures, or Typical Single Channel Test Systems Using Force Control—If the flaw occurs in a non-redundant structure (as is the situation with a link in a chain), there will be no opportunity for the flawed element to "shed" its load. In this case, the initiation point of a significant flaw and the failure of the structure are so close (due to the exponential rise in crack tip stress intensity with flaw size), that propagation is an academic matter, and the key to life prediction (and enhancement) is mainly in the initiation phase, Fig. 25. It is very important to realize that this is what one obtains with testing carried out on single-channel force controlled testing systems.

Redundant Structures, or Displacement-Controlled Test Systems— When a flaw occurs in an element of a redundant structure, the element can by definition "shed" part of its load to adjacent element. In this case, the propagation phase can be quite the more predominant phase in the life of the element, Fig. 26.

In this case, the coupling of finite element techniques with the flaw or notch configurations present in the structure, (for example, a weapon or

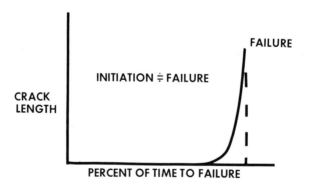

FIG. 25—*Development of fatigue damage in non-redundant structures and in force-controlled fatigue machines.*

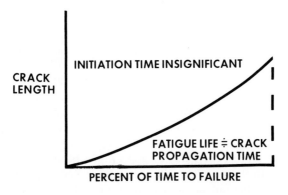

FIG. 26—*Development of fatigue damage with redundant structures or displacement-controlled fatigue machines.*

support structure) will provide the necessary stress intensity factors for projected growth of the flaw. Several computer programs for this approach exist, and it is the most promising for the study of flaw growth.

The rational steps in the development of the fatigue life for the redundant element then can be viewed in the reverse order. That is, the critical flaw size for rapid destruction of the structure is determined. This is the end point on a plot of flaw growth rate versus stress intensity factor. Then, moving down on a plot such as Fig. 27, to smaller and smaller flaw sizes, one arrives at the size of the flaw for the beginning of a specific operational life. This technique must, of course, take into consideration

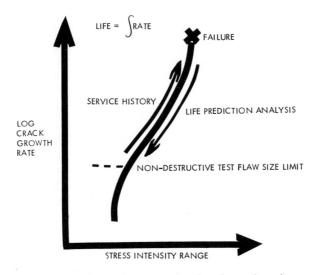

FIG. 27—*Crack-growth rate as a function of stress intensity.*

the gradual decrease in load in the element during the cracking. Few flaw growth studies do this at present. Nevertheless, their results can be used by assuming that prior history does not significantly affect the relation between stress intensity factor and crack growth. If this assumption is made, it is easy to set up a step-wise computer analysis of incremental flaw growth. The resulting load levels, due to structural changes in such growth, the corresponding crack growth rates, and hence the incremental number of cycles (or minutes of complex wave loading) to cover such an increment in flaw growth, can be evaluated.

One can see that in the study of any fatigue problem, careful attention must be taken to define what failure is, and hence what the end point of "life" really is. The end points can be quite different, depending on the redundancy of the structural design. For this reason, current arguments about the relative importance of initiation compared with propagation are academic. In the practical case, one simply determines beforehand the proportion of time that will be spent in each of the two categories of fatigue damage and then concentrates his attention on whichever is the overriding aspect.

4.2.4. Closed Loop Control

Closed-loop control of fatigue testing systems is accomplished by sensing the magnitude of both the controlled and, in some cases, uncontrolled parameters during the execution of the test and transmitting this information (feedback) to the controls where the instantaneous values of the parameters are compared to the programmed (or desired) values of those parameters. The controls automatically adjust the drive system so that the difference between the desired excitation and the excitation transferred to the specimen is reduced to an acceptable level. For example, servocontrolled hydraulic actuators apply a time-varying displacement to a fatigue specimen, but pressure sensors (or a load cell) can detect changes in the maximum or minimum force and through feedback circuits, automatically adjust the controls so that the forces are maintained at the desired level, regardless of the change in specimen stiffness associated with crack growth.

In order to describe briefly the principle of closed-loop control, reference is made to Fig. 28. The signal generator supplies a command signal in the form of a continuous voltage (an analog signal). This signal is amplified and sent to the servovalve, which translates the electronic signal into a mechanical force or deflection, using some form of actuator. The actuator is connected to the test piece. The test piece has in series with it a load cell or other type of transducer, possibly in parallel (such as a displacement transducer).

The action of loading or straining the specimen or moving the actuator causes an analogue voltage signal to be generated from the transducer.

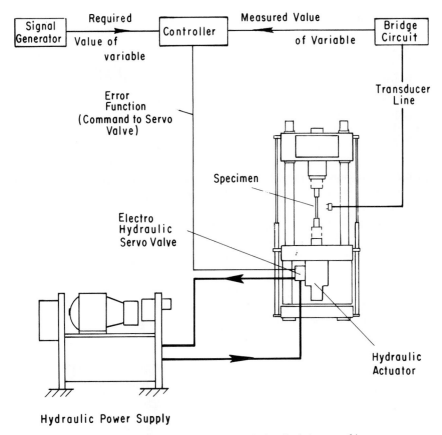

FIG. 28—*Schematic diagram of servo-hydraulic fatigue machine.*

This output signal is brought back to a summing point, at the point where the command signal entered the system, usually with some form of conditioning to make the signals compatible.

At the summing point, the feedback signal from the transducer is given opposite polarity to the command signal from the program. The difference between the two signals is used to drive the actuator in the direction to make this difference zero, as a correction signal. Whether the servocontroller is a carrier-wave type or a direct-current type, it is forever trying to make the difference between program command and transducer feedback equal to zero. Since the transducer is experiencing load or deflection to produce its signal, the preceding electrical discussion of servocontrol is actually creating a mechanical servocontrol.

Closed loop control then involves automatic comparison with a preset program.

The use of different feedback signals often results in quite different behavior from the test specimen. Figure 29 shows the stress-strain behavior of a material being fatigue-cycled in load control (between two limits of loading). Because the loading has a tension bias (the mean value is above the origin), the strain indication shows that the material is "creeping" (elongating) gradually.

A quite different behavior is indicated in Fig. 30. Here the test is carried out in strain control. This means that the specimen is cycled between limits of elongation. The elongation limits here also have a bias to a "tensile" elongation. However, as the cycling continues, the material is able to relax preferentially to reduce the mean tensile stress to zero, and end up with a hysteresis loop which has equal excursions above and below the load axis.

In closed-loop systems where some form of displacement (for example, specimen total strain, or specimen plastic strain component) is used for the feedback signal, it is possible to study a number of interesting phenomena in materials such as strain hardening or softening, and stress or load relaxation. Such systems can use either longitudinal displacements (for example, parallel to round specimen axis) or lateral displacement (strain at the diameter of the specimen).

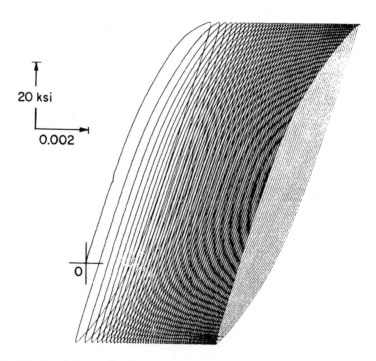

FIG. 29—*A typical example of a load-controlled low cycle fatigue test involving creep.*

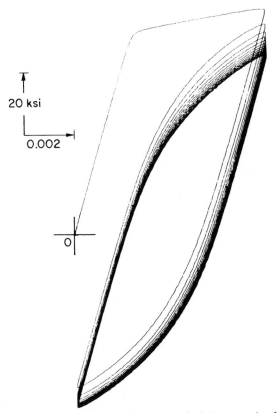

20 ksi

0.002

0

FIG. 30—*An example of a strain-controlled low cycle fatigue test involving mean stress relaxation.*

In soft energy transfer systems, the command signal is indirectly applied through a "soft" field, such as an inductive field and resonances, overshoots and a certain amount of latitude between desired and actual specimens loading can occur. In hard systems, for example, those using incompressible fluids, each position can be made as close to the desired position as required, under normal circumstances. That is why hard systems are also known as "displacement" systems.

The inputs to the servo controller, command and feedback, are signal voltages having the same scaling, usually expressed in millivolts per pound. The servo controller compares these signals. If their instantaneous amplitudes and polarities are not the same, an error signal, or correction signal, is applied to the servovalve. The correction signal is directly proportional to the difference between command and feedback. Since the servo controller provides the power to control the servovalve, its output at full-scale is rated in terms of electrical power, for example, 40 mW or 15 mV into 200 ohms, the input impedance of typical servovalves.

Most servo controllers for mechanical applications are of the "proportional control" type, where the correction is proportional to the error (rather than a simple on-off control). The "gain" of a controller is simply the amount of error needed to provide full output from the controller. "Proportional droop" in a servo controller is the difference between the command and feedback left after the servo control has stabilized at a given value. The proportional band is another name for this region. Ideally, the proportional band should be zero as quickly as possible, after a command is given.

By increasing the amplifier gain in the controller, the sensitivity of the controller is increased. This reduces proportional band and stabilizing time. Unfortunately, there is an upper limit to the degree of proportional sensitivity that the servo system can tolerate without becoming unstable with divergent oscillation of the system. The optimum degree of gain is a function of the stiffness of the complete specimen-machine system. For this reason, most closed-loop systems have adjustable gain settings and stabilizer adjustments.

It is important for the reader to realize, however, that in many displacement-excited systems with some form of force sensing and feedback (partially closed loop), only one of the two levels—maximum or minimum force—is continuously maintained at the programmed level. The amplitude applied to the specimen is still one of fixed displacement. Therefore, the force amplitude decreases with a decrease in specimen stiffness resulting from fatigue-crack growth. In contrast to partially closed-loop systems, fully closed-loop, displacement-excited systems maintain both the maximum and minimum levels of force throughout the test and, consequently, afford increased accuracy to the investigator.

4.2.5. Energy Transfer

The fidelity of the drive system to reproduce the command input signal (the program) as a time-varing specimen excitation is a function of the energy transfer of the system. Test machines vary greatly in their mode of transferring energy to the test specimen. An idea of what is involved in such energy transfer is to imagine the resulting stress pattern on a specimen when the programming signal is a square wave (Fig. 17). If there is rigid coupling, the specimen will experience a square-wave loading. A soft energy-transfer system (such as an electromagnetic field) will be incapable of supplying the rigidity necessary, and the square wave will result in a "rounded-off" signal from the specimen (as its response).

A most common configuration for hard energy-transfer fatigue machines is the eccentric crank connected to a cantilever to impose alternating displacements of a set value to the cantilever specimen. Since the specimen is gripped and connected mechanically to the linkage causing the displacements, the transfer of energy from the machine is "hard;" that is, there is a distinct unique position for the specimen at each point in the displacement cycle in contrast to, say, the position of a driver coil in an electrodynamic shaker due to an imposed current. Adjustment of the crank throw controls the amplitude of deflection, and adjustment of the connecting rod controls the mean displacement of the specimen.

In addition to the eccentric crank drive for cantilever bending, hard-drive systems include axial-load machines with a deflection-calibrated bar lever, such as shown in Fig. 31, hydraulic actuators, and screw power. In each case, the specimen is subjected to deflection or strain control.

FIG. 31—*Schematic of a typical eccentric crank machine.*

When the control parameter is the displacement of the specimen, specimens tested in such machines experience a decrease of load as crack propagation reduces the stiffness near the end of a test. Similarly, specimens that undergo significant plastic deformation are likely to experience a steadily varying history of load cycles because of work-hardening or softening. Some machines are equipped with limit switches to stop the machine when the load changes more than a specific amount.

Most machines of this type, however, are essentially "open loop." That means that there is no feedback of specimen behavior to alter the command other than the limit switch arrangement just mentioned.

Electromagnetic shakers, hydraulic pulsators, combinations of springs and unbalanced rotating masses, hydraulic actuators with load control, and rotating bending machines are all examples of test systems with soft-drive systems. In each case, these machines subject the specimens to load-control conditions (for example, Fig. 32).

4.2.5.1. Hydraulic Actuators—Hydraulic actuators, although they require high precision in design and craftsmanship for fatigue testing, are the most readily understood of all the axial test systems. Fluid under pressure is applied to one side of a piston and the piston moves. If the piston rod contacts some external reaction point, then a force is applied to

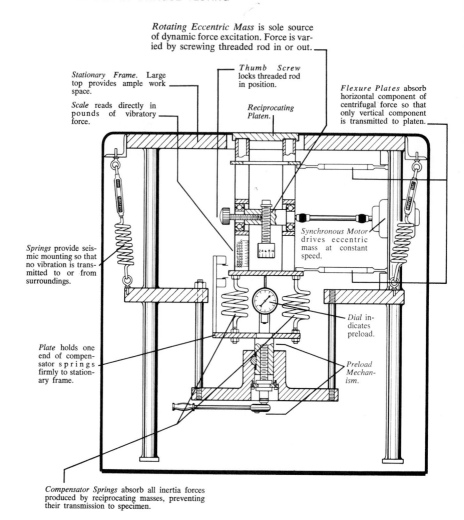

Rotating Eccentric Mass is sole source of dynamic force excitation. Force is varied by screwing threaded rod in or out.

Stationary Frame. Large top provides ample work space.

Scale reads directly in pounds of vibratory force.

Thumb Screw locks threaded rod in position.

Reciprocating Platen.

Flexure Plates absorb horizontal component of centrifugal force so that only vertical component is transmitted to platen.

Springs provide seismic mounting so that no vibration is transmitted to or from surroundings.

Synchronous Motor drives eccentric mass at constant speed.

Plate holds one end of compensator springs firmly to stationary frame.

Dial indicates preload.

Preload Mechanism.

Compensator Springs absorb all inertia forces produced by reciprocating masses, preventing their transmission to specimen.

This view of eccentric mass shows how force is varied by threaded rod. The end of this weight is the index of the scale at the left, which reads directly in pounds force. A circumferential scale is graduated on the weight, reading in tenths of a turn.

FIG. 32—*Example of a soft energy transfer/open loop test system.*

that point that is equal to the effective piston area times the actuating pressure.

The main criteria for selecting an actuator are the force and stroke required by the test parameters. However, the problem remains simple only for low-rate or low-frequency tests. At higher frequencies, factors such as servovalve response, fluid compressibility, oil column resonance, inertia of the piston, and the mass attached to the piston make the problems of selecting actuator-servovalve combinations more complex. The high-pressure piston seal is usually omitted for very high speed applications.

Another aspect peculiar to all devices involving sliding is called "stiction." This is a term coined to refer to the situation when an actuator will stick in a given position. This is due to the fact that the coefficient of friction at the sliding surfaces can be significant at low speeds, and can cause an abrupt stoppage of the piston. Pressure will finally cause the piston to move again. However, the loading on piston travel will not be as smooth as desired. To minimize the possibility of stiction, a high frequency, insignificantly low amplitude signal is added to the command signal, called a "dither" signal.

The low-leakage viscous and labyrinth groove seals shown in Fig. 33 are typically provided on both the rod and piston through the use of labyrinth grooves and close tolerance fits. This seal is effective whenever the high pressure seals are omitted for high speed cyclic applications. It is also an excellent backup should the high pressure seals wear out, in which case it permits continued operation of the actuator with only a slight decrease in performance.

The servovalve for hydraulic actuators—Figure 34 shows a common servovalve drive for a hydraulic actuator. The rating of the servovalve is usually expressed in gallons per minute (gpm) at a specified pressure drop. Even when fully open, the valve represents two orifices through which the fluid between the supply and the actuator must flow. One orifice "ports" high-pressure fluid, P, to one side of the actuator's piston and the other provides a path for return, R, flow (low pressure) from the other side of the piston to the supply. The orifices offer a resistance to flow, just as a resistor offers a resistance to current flow in an electrical circuit. Thus, the flow rating of a given servovalve may be expressed as "15 gpm at 1000 psi drop." As just stated, the electrical input requirements of the servovalve, for full rated flow (valve fully open), are usually expressed in terms of power or as "so many milliamps of current into so many ohms of resistance."

The servovalve converts an electrical signal into a mechanical action, changing the direction of fluid flow in the actuator, through the twist of a small electro-magnetic torque motor.

The combined servovalve actuator performance is expressed by the following equation

$$X = \frac{\dfrac{1.23Q}{f} - \dfrac{VP}{2K}}{A}$$

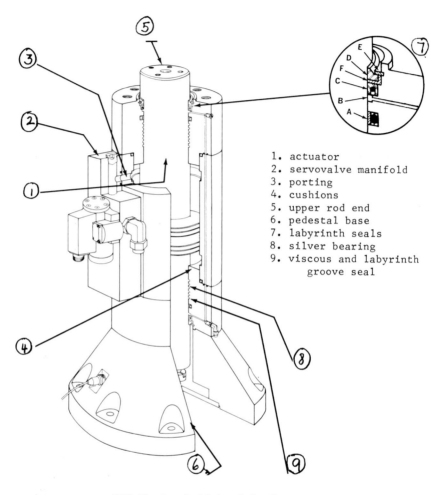

1. actuator
2. servovalve manifold
3. porting
4. cushions
5. upper rod end
6. pedestal base
7. labyrinth seals
8. silver bearing
9. viscous and labyrinth
    groove seal

FIG. 33—*A typical fatigue hydraulic actuator.*

where

X = double displacement amplitude, in.,
f = frequency, Hz,
Q = servovalve peak flow, gpm,
V = total oil volume between servovalve and actuator piston, in.^{3},
P = peak differential pressure across actuator piston, psi, and
K = bulk modulus of the hydraulic fluid, psi.

The servo amplifier provides an adjustable control gain to the control loop. The inverse of this gain is sometimes called "proportional band." Proportional band is the percentage of feedback error necessary to achieve full servovalve opening. The control response and accuracy improves with

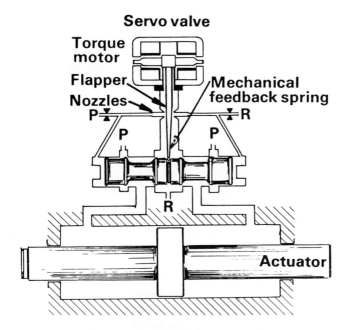

FIG. 34—*A typical "flapper" type servovalve.*

decreasing proportional band (increasing gain). Unfortunately, there is a limit to the amount of gain the servo system will tolerate without producing severe overshoot (over-correction to an input command) and eventual instability with divergent oscillation of the system.

A problem occurs when the servovalve is too large for the application, and thus has too high a hydraulic gain. As electronic gain is reduced to maintain loop stability, the threshold level (about one percent of full drive) of the servovalve becomes significant, as related to proportional band, and the proportional band becomes wider. The system seems "mushy" and the controlled variable may drift noticeably while under set point conditions. In addition, the drive to the servovalve is proportionally reduced to the point where the valve may never open fully and thus will not realize its full flow potential.

To avoid these problems on standard systems which must perform well over a wide range of conditions without special circuitry or tuning, a good "rule of thumb" is to keep the servovalve flow (gpm) equal to, or less than, actuator rating (kips).

This rule is safe for almost all systems with valves having a 10 gpm rating or less. The rule should be modified for larger (and less responsive) valves as shown in the following.

Servovalve flow rating, gpm	5	10	15	25	40	60
Actuator rating, kips	5	10	20	40	75	120

The rule is based on "stiff" systems such as are used for metal specimen testing in a load frame, and can be amended to include larger valves when the following conditions exist.

1. Where the load train is "soft" enough so that the maximum frequency at full load excursions is less than 30 Hz, for small valves, and less than 10 Hz for large valves.

2. Where ideal mechanical conditions prevail: low moving mass, no low resonant frequencies in the loop, and no mechanical backlash or loose joints.

3. When special electronic optimizing or trimming circuits are utilized.

The fluid flow available to the servovalve from the hydraulic power supply can have a great effect on the high frequency fatigue cycling capability of the test system (Fig. 35).

Further details of the systems are subsequently described. However, it is reiterated that different failure lifetimes can be expected under similar elastic strain or load histories for soft and hard systems.

4.2.6. Energy Conservation

Fatigue testing systems may be classified with respect to the degree of conservation of external driving energy required to excite the specimen. There are three general categories: (1) conservative systems in which some of the strain energy in the specimen upon unloading is returned to the drive system; (2) resonant systems in which force amplification is achieved

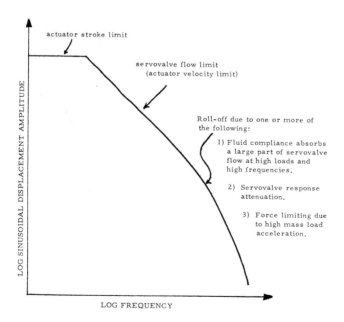

FIG. 35—*Typical maximum displacement response of loaded servo-hydraulic actuator.*

by exciting a tuned specimen-machine system at or near its resonant frequency; and (3) nonconservative, or "brute-force," systems in which the strain energy released during the unloading of the specimen is not returned to the drive system.

Conservative systems include crank-driven fatigue machines where the rotary motion of a cam or flywheel is converted to a reciprocating displacement to excite the specimen. The strain energy released by the specimen during unloading is stored in the rotating element of the machine, thus requiring relatively low power input. Another conservative system is the hydraulic pulsator which is, essentially, a variable stroke hydraulic pump converting rotary motion to reciprocation displacement. As in the crank-driven machine, strain energy released during the unloading of the specimen is returned to the flywheel of the pump, thus conserving energy and requiring relatively low power input. Conservative systems serve best as constant-amplitude fatigue machines. Programming such systems for variable-amplitude tests is usually limited to schedules in which load amplitude vary slowly relative to time. Stepwise changes in load amplitude are usually subjected to significant transients.

Resonance testing systems may be divided into two general groups: (1) Sub-resonant systems that operate just below the resonant frequency of the specimen-machine system (that is, on the rising slope of the force amplitude-frequency curve, Point A, Fig. 36) and (2) resonant machines which operate at the resonant frequency of the specimen-machine system (that is. at the top of the force amplitude-frequency curve, Point B. Fig. 36). Operations at subresonance may be achieved by holding the mass of moving elements constant and regulating the speed. It may be seen in Fig. 36 that slight fluctuations in speed at frequencies well away from the resonant frequency cause only small variations in load amplitude. However, similar variations in operating speed at frequencies near

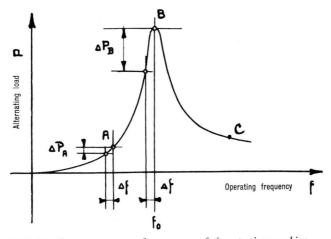

FIG. 36—*Resonance curve of a resonance fatigue testing machine.*

resonance can cause significant variations in load amplitude. It is desirable in the latter case to tune the system by varying the mass of the moving elements rather than varying the driving frequency. Another cause of load fluctuation is the change in resonant frequency of the system due to a decrease in specimen stiffness as the crack grows. Resonant and subresonant systems include crank-driven, rotating-mass, electromagnetic, and servocontrolled-electrohydraulic machines.

It should be pointed out that Fig. 36 represents the dynamic response of fatigue testing systems in general and not just those designed to operate at or near resonance. Most systems will operate at Point A, but systems operating above resonance, Point C, are not uncommon. For example, hydraulic pulsators with long, relatively flexible, hydraulic delivery lines and flexible specimens may pass through resonance, Point B, during the transient startup and operate at Point C.

Loading systems which do not conserve the energy released by the specimen during unloading have become known as "brute-force" systems. These systems require a continual supply of energy to be introduced into the system and, therefore, consume relatively large amounts of power. Most machines in this category are readily programmable and give the investigator the widest range of capabilities of all fatigue testing systems. Examples of nonconservative systems include mechanical screw-driven machines, electromagnetic shakers, and servocontrolled-electrohydraulic systems.

The application of resonant systems and nonconservative systems to structural fatigue testing is discussed in Chapter 10.

4.3 Axial-Load Fatigue-Testing Systems

Axial-load fatigue-testing systems subject the test specimens to a stress (or strain) distribution that, for an unnotched specimen, is reasonably uniform throughout the cross section. However, precise axial loading is difficult to achieve under normal test conditions. For the same size specimens, axial-load systems must be capable of applying greater forces than bending machines to achieve the same maximum stress (or strain). The major advantage of the axial-load system is that it produces a relatively uniform load distribution over a relatively large volume of material in the specimen, thus eliminating the perturbing effects of the stress (or strain) gradient present in the bending test. In addition, fatigue testing in the plastic range can be precisely evaluated in the case of axial-load testing.

4.3.1 Mechanical Drive Systems

Machines, such as shown in Fig. 31, apply a cyclic load to one end of a specimen by a deflection-calibrated bar lever. In some of these machines the specimen is in series with a hydraulic load-maintainer piston which, by sensing the creep in the specimen, steplessly restores the test loading. This type of machine is partially "closed loop" since the mean load is continuously corrected. See Fig. 37 for another diagram of an axial load machine utilizing an eccentric crank.

Many types of hard/open loop systems involve cams and hydraulic actuators. A great many of these machines have been developed over the years.

Constant displacement amplitude devices, being "hard systems," only require that the specimen deform sufficiently to satisfy the displacements programmed for the test. In extreme cases, this can be accomplished by the growth of a crack to a certain size, and the specimen then can run indefinitely with a nonpropagating crack in it. While this is an extreme example, it does emphasize the load amplitude reduction that is often present in constant displacement devices. Of course, while the specimen is unflawed and is strained elastically there is no difference between soft and hard systems. Once inelastic behavior begins, however, the specimen tested in a hard system often will "last" much longer due to load relaxation. The period of crack propagation will be longer than is the case with the identical specimen tested in the identical mode in a soft system where there is no load relaxation.

In a sense then, hard systems can give one unsafe estimates of life, if the service situation is "soft" (non-redundant design), while the test situation is hard. This problem is overcome by examining the service situation carefully, and choosing the type of fatigue test device to suit the hardness of the service application.

Use has been made of hard systems for comparing material behavior under S-N conditions where the prior precautions do not apply.

One area where hard/open loop systems have been utilized extensively, is in the area of multiple specimen testing (Ref *18*). It has always been attractive to fatigue test designers to replicate tests as efficiently as possible. The basic "parallel" nature of hard systems (as opposed to the "series" nature of soft systems) means that, ideally, the failure of one

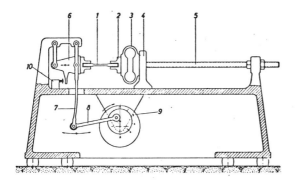

1. Specimen
2. Specimen grips
3. Load proving ring.
4. Fixed head assembly
5. Mean load spindle
6. Moving head assembly
7. Load lever
8. Connecting rod
9. Variable cam motor
10. Shut-down contact

FIG. 37—*Schematic illustration of another fatigue machine using eccentric throw.*

specimen does not affect the performance of the machine, since it is meeting displacement criteria independent of the condition of the specimen. Since this is an ideal situation, it is rarely met in practice, since there is always some degree of softness in the test system (especially in systems involving soft energy transfer such as electromagnets).

4.3.2 Electromagnetic Shakers

A very common fatigue device of this type is the electromagnetic exciter, which is used either as the primary drive and is then capable of broad band excitation, or is used to excite a mass or inertia system to resonance in which case it is capable of single-peak resonance or two-peak resonance at best. In the direct mode, they are capable of Type F signals. The following paragraphs outline their basic principle of operation.

The means of achieving transformation of energy is the basic electromagnetic phenomenon of current flow I through a conductor that is in a magnetic field causing a force to be exerted on the conductor, Fig. 38. The force is related to current by Eq 1.

$$F = 0.885 \times 10^{-7} \, BLI \tag{1}$$

where B is the magnetic flux density in lines per square inch and L is the length of current-carrying conductor in inches. The flux density and length of conductor are held constant in shakers and the force is directly proportional to the current I. If the current carrying conductor is allowed to move in the magnetic field a back voltage is induced in it that is directly proportional to the velocity of the conductor.

This earliest form of shakers was called the top gap end shaker which resembled a loudspeaker. This style of shaker had a relatively short armature, but the size of this shaker compared to the force output was rather large because the flux density was limited by saturation of the iron. The optimum geometry was approximately a gap height equal to one fourth of the coil diameter. The major problem with the top gap end shaker was the high stray magnetic field appearing at the table.

The next step in shaker development was to use another coil mounted on top of a top gap end shaker to set up a counter magnetic field to the

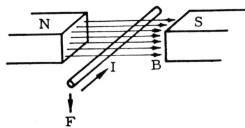

FIG. 38—*Current carrying conductor in magnetic field.*

stray field. This additional coil is referred to as a degaussing coil. The limitation of this method was the very large d-c power requirement of the degaussing coil to counteract the very strong stray field and the heat dissipation that resulted.

The modern design is called the double ended shaker, Fig. 39. The magnetic circuit in this design is doubled and the optimum geometry is a gap height equal to one-half the diameter of the armature coil. The armature of the double-ended design is much better dynamically and is capable of quite a wide operational frequency range. The magnetic circuit is completely enclosed and only a very small degaussing coil is used to minimize the stray field to a negligible amount.

The flexures in double-ended shakers are usually many laminations of beryllium copper that form rolls or half rolls around the perimeter of the armature table. These flexures support the armature in the body of the shaker and provide a stiffness that is about one hundred times greater in the lateral direction than in the axial direction. The axial stiffness is chosen to support a specimen load weight equal to the armature weight without external support and still to be able to have a displacement of 1 in. double amplitude. This axial stiffness causes the resonance of the armature mass and flexures to fall between 10 Hz and 20 Hz.

Some of the newer designs use compressed air for supporting the armature and specimen. This allows full displacement on a specimen that is much heavier than the armature without external support. Hydrostatic bearings are used in these shakers to provide a high degree of lateral stiffness.

Shakers are generally limited in their force capabilities by the heat generated in the shaker. Therefore, cooling is an important part of a shaker. Shakers that have force ratings less than 25 and 1500 lb are cooled by forced air. Shakers above 1500 lb are most efficiently cooled by a closed distilled water system with a pump, reservoir, and heat exchanger. The water cooling method allows forces up to 30 000 lb to be obtained from a single shaker. The heat transfer to the water is made

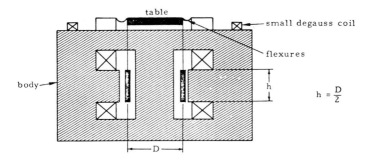

FIG. 39—*Double ended shaker.*

directly because the armature coil and field coils are hollow tubing through which the water is conveyed.

4.3.3 Pulsators

For fatigue loading, a hydraulic jack (or jacks) can be connected to a "pulsator." This machine consists essentially of a pump with one large piston of continuously adjustable stroke. The working principle is shown schematically in Fig. 40. The minimum pressure is supplied by a small piston pump (6) delivering oil into the main cylinder (5) over the regulating valve (7). By changing the force of spring (8) the minimum pressure is changed accordingly. The pulsating pressure is produced by the movement of the main piston (4). The stroke is controlled by a three-bar linkage system. Position A and B of bar (2) determine the maximum and minimum piston stroke. On its upward stroke, the piston (4) forces oil from the pulsator into the jack. On the downward stroke the elasticity of the test specimen pushes the oil back into the pulsator. Therefore, the same quantity of oil flows back and forth between pulsator and jack. With no valves and by-passes such a system has very smooth and quiet operating characteristics producing an almost perfect sinusoidal pressure variation in the hydraulic jack.

There are two basic types of pulsators: single and double-acting.

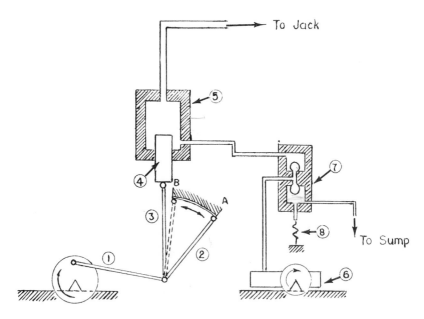

FIG. 40—*Schematic diagram of pulsator.*

Single acting pulsators can apply loads on one side of zero only. However, in some machines a testing head is equipped with a secondary piston accumulator system to apply a steady force equal to the desired maximum force in one direction. The pulsator then acts in opposition to this force to produce load cycles that may pass through zero. When a double-acting pulsator is used reversed loads may be applied without a secondary system. In such a system a mean load may be applied by the introduction of a bias pressure on the system.

Programming of pulsator devices is usually limited to schedules in which load amplitudes vary slowly so that a cam control can be used. Stepwise changes in load are usually subjected to significant transients.

4.4 Bending Machines

It is difficult to tell which has been the most common form of fatigue machine, either the rotating beam or the repeated flexure (repeated bend) device. Certainly, for sheer numbers of machines, these two types, with innumerable variations must represent the two most common types.

Bending fatigue machines are usually considered appropriate for studies of the surface of the specimen, in that the surface is strained the most. They are also commonly used for materials which are basically sheet form. One version of a displacement control bending machine is shown in Fig. 41.

Since the bending moment varies linearly along a cantilever, the specimens used in bending test usually are linearly tapered in width to permit a section of the specimen to have uniform extreme fiber strain.

The main problem area with bending machines is usually in the gripping. The clamping often causes excessive fretting, and failure can occur in the gripped ends of the specimen. Also small amounts of twist in the specimen due to misalignment of the clamping axes can produce non-normal endurances. Antichafing inserts are sometimes used in the grips, but care must be taken to ensure that the fixity of the grip is not altered by this modification.

Another area where problems can arise with bend specimens is in the edges. Since the material is in the form of flat plate, the cross-section is usually rectangular. Failure of the specimen is rather sensitive to the condition of the corners presented by the specimen cross-section. In tests with this type of device, mention must be made of the condition of the corners.

Stress determination in hard systems in bending usually relies on knowing the appropriate modulus of elasticity, while load cells are commonly used in axial loading. Since cycling and damping can affect the bending modulus appreciably, especially at large values of displacement, it is difficult to know the stress history with much accuracy using indirect calculations.

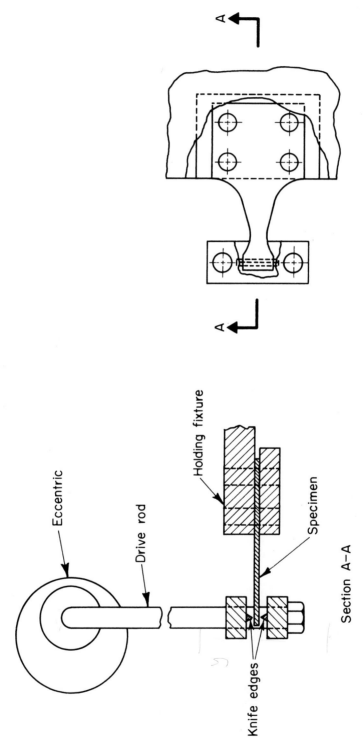

FIG. 41—*Schematic diagram of plate bending fatigue machine.*

Some bending machines of the hard/open loop variety are considered capable of non-zero mean stress by imposing a fixed displacement in the cantilever specimen at the beginning before vibrating the specimen about this new position. This is very unsatisfactory for fundamental work, since in reality the mean stress on one side of the specimen is of opposite sign to the mean stress on the opposite side of the specimen. .

Basic studies in fatigue usually shun gradients of loading in the material, and strive for spatially uniform stress conditions at any given instant.

Non-resonant bending machines are inherently slow in accumulating cycles compared to rotating beam machines. Also, the strain gradient under bending loading can cause data interpretation problems for fatigue testing in the plastic range.

4.4.1 Rotating Beam Machines

This test device is a very simple and efficient means of inducing fatigue in a specimen of round cross section. It is the traditional form of fatigue machine, having been used by A. Woehler in his classic work on the fatigue of railway axles in the 1850's (frontispiece). Rotating beams are exactly what is involved in the railway axle fatigue problem. Unfortunately, the study of fatigue has shown that mode of loading has a significant effect on fatigue life; consequently, data from a rotating beam test may not be applicable for many design usages.

In a rotating beam test, a dead-weight-induced steady load is applied to the specimen as a cantilever with four-point bending yokes. Bearings are provided to permit rotation of the specimen. The stress at a given point on the surface of the specimen will undergo a sinusoidal change in value about a zero point, with equal excursions in tension and compression. Type A loading is the only loading normally possible with such equipment.

As an example, four R.R. Moore rotating bending fatigue machines are shown in Fig. 42. Essentially, they consist of a high speed motor, a pair of housings supported so as to give a constant bending moment over the length of the specimen, a flexible coupling between the motor and one housing, a series of weights in sizes from 0.1 to 10 lb, and a yoke used to apply the load to the specimen. The operating speed of the motors was 10 000 rpm. The maximum moment which could be applied to the specimen was 200 in·lb, this being achieved with 90 lb of removable weights on the weight hangers. The resulting maximum stress available was approximately 150 ksi in the specimens used.

Due to the relatively small size of the test specimen test area, only a small volume of material is subjected to significant cyclic stress. For fatigue testing in the plastic range, this strain gradient can be troublesome from the standpoint of precisely interpreting the test results. In rotating

FIG. 42—(a) *Rotating beam test apparatus—general layout.* (b) *Rotating beam test apparatus—close-up of specimen area.*

beam machines that are driven from one end, the test specimen must transmit the torque to overcome the friction in the outboard bearings, hence the stress state in the specimen is not exactly unidirectional. This friction torque is more significant in constant bending moment machines than in cantilever machines.

As an additional point, the cost of machining rotating beam specimens is comparatively high, considering the small volume of material that is effectively being subjected to fatigue testing.

In the cantilever arrangement the bending moment applied to the test specimen varies linearly with the distance from the load application point, and the specimen is also subjected to a transverse shearing load. Cantilever rotating beam machines are rather versatile, in regard to the size of test specimen that can be accommodated, since only a single load acting through a rotating bearing at the free end is required. This arrangement is well suited for environmental type tests, such as corrosion fatigue testing, since the machine and specimen structural requirements at the free end are not too critical. On the other hand, the fixed end position can be troublesome for both the bearing and the specimen, because of the high bending moment. In order to preclude fretting fatigue failure at the fixed end position, the dimensions of the specimen at this location should be increased sufficiently to ensure low nominal stress; surface treatments, such as cold rolling, can be incorporated to enhance the fretting fatigue strength at the grip. To offset the effect of the variable applied bending moment on specimen stressing, it is possible to design a tapered specimen so that essentially uniform stressing is obtained in the test section.

Special Rotating Beam Machines—Wire Testers—There are several types of wire testers working on the principle of a rotating "beam." In this case, the "beam" is a length of wire curved between two grips so that the stress is highest away from the grips.

In determining the fatigue properties of wire, it is usually essential to avoid disturbing the surface of the wire in any way. This precludes the possibility of preparing specimens with a reduced section. To reduce or eliminate the incidence of grip failures in specimens of constant cross-section, wire is usually tested in reversed bending.

The most common reversed bending fatigue test of wire stresses the specimen as a buckled strut, rotating about the buckled axis, Fig. 43. The wire is mounted in a chuck on the motor at A and in a tail stock bearing at B. Fatigue failure will occur in the center of the specimen where the stress is maximum and not at the grips where free rotation of A and B produces a stress-free condition. The applied stress amplitude is computed by one or two methods: (1) measuring the end slope (or rotation) O, and computing the stress from Euler's Elastica or (2) measuring the axial thrust P and deflection d and computing the stress from the maximum bending moment Pd.

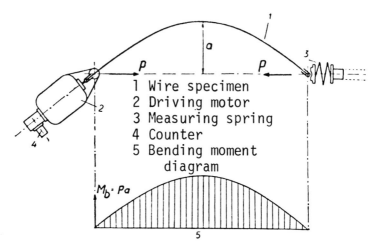

FIG. 43—*Bending moment diagram for wire tester—configuration* (a).

A second type of reversed bending fatigue test for wire is shown in Fig. 44. In this test, the specimen is subjected to a constant bending moment along its entire length by end-couples applied to the end bearings. However, this test scheme is not free from grip failures and, in addition, it

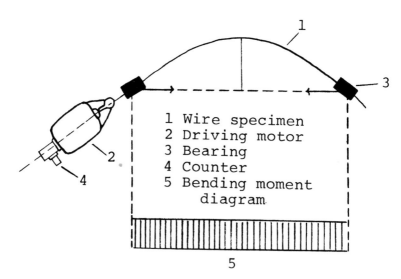

FIG. 44—*Bending moment diagram for wire tester—configuration* (b).

is often found necessary to immerse the middle portion of the wire in an oil bath to damp vibrations. The latter point can be used to advantage when performing corrosion fatigue tests of wire by replacing the oil bath by a corrosive fluid.

Both bending fatigue tests just described require that the wire specimens be straightened before testing. Rotary-arbor swaging is preferred over tensile yielding in a tensile testing machine.

4.5 Rolling Contact Fatigue

Numerous devices using either a roller or ball specimen have been constructed to attain a simple bench-type rig for testing for rolling contact fatigue. Such devices have been useful in evaluating the contact fatigue characteristics of materials used in gears, cams, and rolling element bearings, and for studying the influence of geometric shape and processing on such materials.

Full-scale performance testing of manufactured parts, such as gears and rolling bearings, have been conducted on a variety of special purpose machines.

4.5.1 Rolling Contact Bench Rigs

There is little uniformity as yet to the approaches taken in bench rig testing relative to specimen design, test procedures, or machine design. Machines used are of four main types.

(a) One roller drives another roller by friction and the normal force as described in Refs 19 and 20.

(b) Both rollers are drivers, and various degrees of sliding may be introduced in the contact by selection of gears connecting the roller shafts as described in Refs 21 and 22.

(c) Multiple-point rolling contact, where a test roller drives the load roller, or one or more load rollers drives a roller or ball test specimen as described in References 23, 24, and 25, respectively.

(d) Simulated bearing test, using a ball specimen driver loaded by a circle of three to four balls rotating in a race [26 and 27], or a nonrotating flat washer specimen loaded by a partial complement of balls in a thrust ball race [28].

The references listed provide detailed information on the specific machine types. Most of the rolling contact machines mentioned have also been used for evaluating the load carrying capacity of lubricants.

Contact fatigue testing for reliable comparative evaluation of materials should be conducted under standardized, controlled conditions of lubrication. A circulating oil system with filtering and temperature control is considered a necessary adjunct to any of the preceding machines.

These are constant load type machines, specimen life being expressed in load-cycles to failure, or Hertzian stress-cycles to failure. Pitting, or spalling, of the specimen surface to an arbitrary criterion is evidenced visually or sensed by breaking a threshold value of unacceptable vibration.

4.6 Gear Testers

Both rotating and nonrotating type machines have been built to investigate the fatigue resistance of actual gears. Both types require careful control of alignment through design and assembly, since maldistribution of load can affect significantly the stress levels produced. In gear testing, the effect of mismatch across the face of the contacting teeth must be considered. Whether due to tooth taper, shaft bending, housing deflection, misalignment of tester, or temperature effects, the maldistribution of load is a serious influence on peak stress levels. Reference *29* describes a preliminary method for determining the effects of misalignment of the load transmitting teeth. These determinations should be made for each load or stress level in the test spectrum, and should include actual deflections of the test rig under load.

In addition to maldistribution, operating stress levels can be intensified in rotating gear testers by dynamic load increments associated with tooth errors, torsional variations in the shafting, and unbalance of rotating element. Determination of peak loads must be made if gear fatigue test data are to be correlated with fatigue strength developed in the more conventional methods. Reference *30* contains the analytical methods required to estimate dynamic load increments. High speed testing makes this problem extremely important, since dynamic loads, five to six times higher than the transmitted loads, have been encountered. Measurement of dynamic loads by strain gage techniques is recommended.

Both rotating and non-rotating testing require accurate measurement of the test specimens to ensure verification of elements used in calculating stress levels. Since commercial and some precision gear manufacturing methods produce occasional parts with serious deviations, it is recommended that careful inspection be performed and that the data be recorded so as to permit identification with each gear (including angular and axial orientation).

Testing of "production" samples is often conducted without the detailed analysis and inspection previously reviewed, but such work is limited to describing average or mean data, requiring careful interpretation and statistical analysis. It is recommended that the detailed procedure be followed since variation so delineated and analyzed will ensure (1) better correlation with fundamental material properties, (2) fuller appreciation of the variations in production gears, and (3) data to support a failure analysis activity.

Through a great number of rotating gear testers, basic needs developed for specific applications as well as general applications. The great majority of these devices fall into a few categories. Since it would be impossible to name and describe all variations, only the more generally used devices will be included.

The more basic rotating testers are four-square (locked torque, back-to-back, etc.), which utilize a circulating load derived from mechanically or hydraulically induced static torque of the shafting. This method is popular because of the low power requirements, since only losses within the system need to be overcome. The mechanically induced load and, therefore, start-up procedures must provide adequate free lubrication to prevent tooth scoring. In addition, careful calibration and setting of torque is necessary to ensure correlation between operating loads, design loads, and indicated fatigue strength.

Conventional rotating gear testers can be used to develop gear contact fatigue properties by careful gear design which ensures against bending fatigue being the controlling mode. Of significant interest is the length and location of the line of action of the mesh being tested. This should be held to that of the service design for which the data are being accumulated, since contact fatigue data are complicated by the lubricant properties.

For the closest correlation of gear fatigue strength with basic material fatigue properties, a number of oscillating and unidirectional loading machines have been developed. These machines offer the advantage of close control of loading direction and intensity, but fail to apply the often neglected compressive loading encountered in actual power transmission systems. One other major advantage is found in the ability to achieve several fatigue failures on an individual gear, thus adding to the statistical significance while eliminating dynamic effects (Fig. 45).

With such non-rotating testers, hydraulic, electrical, or mechanical loading may be employed with control enhanced by the availability of continual load monitoring, since the specimen does not rotate. Care must be taken to account for deflections and load maldistribution as well as long term effects of brinnelling or abrasion. These latter possibilities may ensue if lubrication is not able to prevent wear on the contacting surfaces.

4.6.1 Bearing Tests

Another area of rolling contact fatigue is the field of bearing testers. In this test one or more bearings are mounted in a fixture and the loading is applied through the normal loading races for the bearing (Fig. 46).

As with gear testing, there is often no clear-cut indication of "failure," and such tests must be monitored carefully.

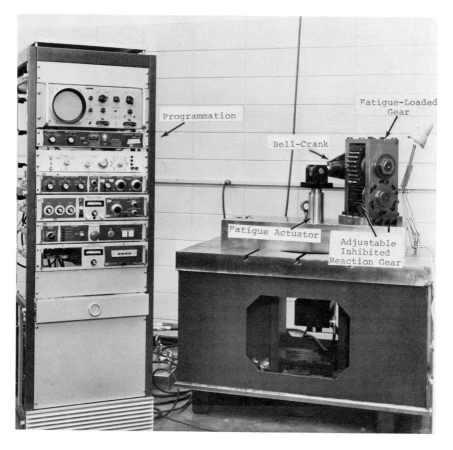

FIG. 45—*A single-tooth gear fatigue test system using a vertical actuator fitted to a bell-crank.*

4.7 Torsion Fatigue Systems

While bending is a mode of loading which can be applied very simply through the modification of a basically axial machine, torsion loading is generally designed into the drive system of the machine to begin with. There are a few exceptions, and Fig. 16 shows an example of a torsion device operated by a basically axial loading drive.

There are many ways to achieve torsional loading, but the main difference in design centers around the extent of twist available for the user. If the twist range is small (up to, say, 280 deg) then rotary actuators can be used. If the twist is smaller still (for example, 100 deg or less) then bell cranks and linear actuators are often used, obtaining the rotary action through levers and linear motion. If the twist is greater than 280 deg, motors are often used, Fig. 47.

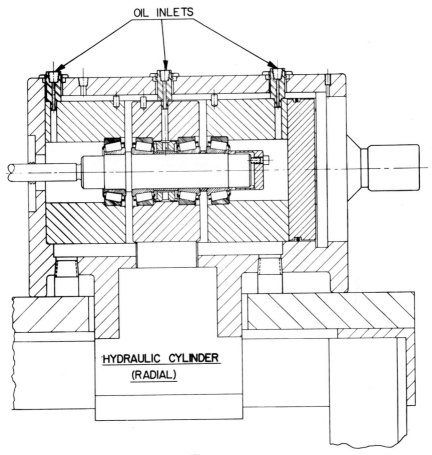

OIL INLETS

HYDRAULIC CYLINDER
(RADIAL)

FIG. 46—*Drawing of a multiple bearing fatigue testing machine.*

The operation of the limited travel rotary is shown in Fig. 48. High pressure fluid enters port (1) connected to chamber (2) which is connected through shaft porting to chamber (3). Fixed abutments (4) and (5), and shaft mounted vanes (6) and (7), force the actuator shaft to rotate counterclockwise. The other chambers (8) and (9) reduce in volume, forcing oil out port (10). Rotation in the opposite direction is obtained by reversing the hydraulic flow from the servovalve. Single vane actuators utilize similar principle but have only one shaft mounted vane and one fixed abutment, Figs. 49 *a* and *b*.

While an effort has been made to describe all the main drives used in fatigue testing, the treatment is essentially incomplete, since there are an "open-ended" number of drives possible. For example, magnetostriction drive is quite possible, and is briefly described in Chapter 9 in connection with corrosion fatigue testing.

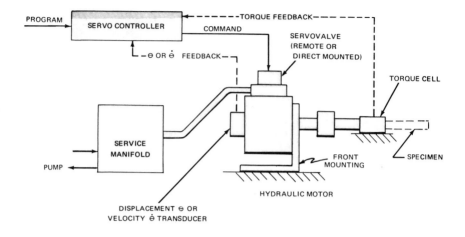

FIG. 47—*Schematic diagram of a torsion fatigue test system using a hydraulic motor.*

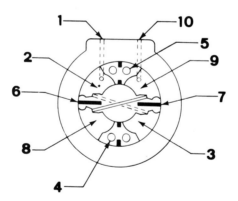

FIG. 48—*Schematic diagram of the operation of the limited-travel rotary actuator.*

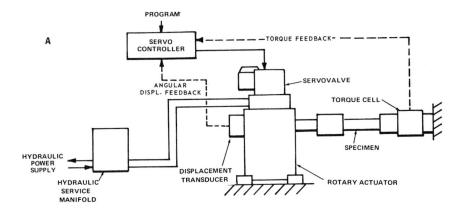

1. RVDT (Rotational Variable
   Differential Transducer
2. Servovalve
3. Actuator
4. Flange coupling

5. Specimen
6. Diaphram-type reaction
   mount
7. Torque Cell

FIG. 49—(a) *Schematic diagram of a torsion fatigue system.* (b) *A photo of a typical torsion fatigue system.*

References

[18] Little, R. E., *Materials Research and Standards,* Vol. 7, No. 1, Jan. 1967, pp. 1-5.

[19] Greenert, W. J., "Toroidal Contact Roller Test as Applied to the Study of Bearing Materials," *Journal of Basic Engineering,* 1962.

[20] Way, S., *Journal of Applied Mechanics,* Vol. 2, No. 2, June 1935, pp. A-49.

[21] Buckingham, E., *Transactions,* American Society of Mechanical Engineers, Vol. 66, No. 4, May 1944, pp. 297-310.

[22] Leach, E. F. and Kelley, B. W., "Temperature—The Key to Lubricant Capacity," ASLE Paper 641C-13, ASLE/ASME International Lubrication Conference, Washington, D.C., 1964.

[23] Baughman, R. A., "Experimental Laboratory Studies of Bearing Fatigue," ASME Paper 58-A-235, 10 Nov. 1958.

[24] McKelvey, R. E. and Moyer, C. A., "The Relation Between Critical Maximum Compressive Stress and Fatigue Life Under Rolling Contact," presented at Institution of Mechanical Engineers Symposium on Fatigue on Rolling Contact, Paper 1, London, 28 March 1963.

[25] Jackson, E. G., *Transactions,* American Society of Lubrication Engineers, Vol. 2, No. 1, 1959, p. 121.

[26] Barwell, F. T. and Scott, D., *Engineering,* Vol. 182, No. 4713, 6 July 1956, p. 9.

[27] Zaretsky, E. V. and Anderson, W. J., "Rolling Contact Fatigue Studies with Four Tool Steels and a Crystallized Glass Ceramic," ASME Lubrication Meeting, New York, 14-15 March 1960.

[28] "The Unisteel Rolling Fatigue Testing Machine (Balls on Flat Washer)," Distington Engineering Company Ltd., Workington, Cumberland, England.

[29] Dudley, Darle, *Practical Gear Design,* McGraw-Hill, New York, 1954.

[30] Buckingham, Earle, *Design Loads on Gear Teeth,* Industrial Press, 1931.

Chapter 5—Drive Systems for Multiaxial and Special Purpose Test Systems

In this chapter, examples are given of fatigue systems and machines which have been designed to apply more than one mode of loading that subjects the specimen to biaxial or triaxial stresses. In addition, there are discussions of a number of special purpose test systems.

Since the system differences for multiaxial loading are based on the loading modes, the appropriate sections of the chapter have been classified in terms of the particular combination of modes involved. It should be noted that, as is the case with attachments for non-axial loading (Section 3.7), there are special specimen shapes which will create multi-axial or biaxial loadings in parts of the specimen using uniaxial test equipment.

As most of the equipment is of a specialized nature, the descriptions given later are relatively brief. For further information, the reader should consult the bibliography given at the end of the chapter.

5.1 Planar Biaxial Tension

Biaxial tension can be obtained by internal pressurization alone, and this system with modifications is discussed in Section 5.3. A system for planar biaxial loading is shown in Fig. 50. Four actuators (X_1, X_2, Y_1, Y_2), running in two servoloops, are used to prevent undesirable distortion of the specimen due to changes in centroid position under loading. The specimens are normally cruciform in shape with a reduced section thickness at the center. They may be loaded through pins or through special wedge grips.

An alternative method that has been used, specifically to simulate the state of stress encountered in pressure-vessel service, is to subject a rectangular plate to hydraulic oil pressure on one side. The plate is freely supported on the edges and uniformly loaded by periodic pulsation of the oil pressure. With such a specimen, the ratio of the two principal stresses on the surface at the center of the plate can be varied by changing the dimensions of the rectangle. Another advantage is that the plate specimen can be tested in the appropriate thickness and with the surfaces essentially in the as-received condition.

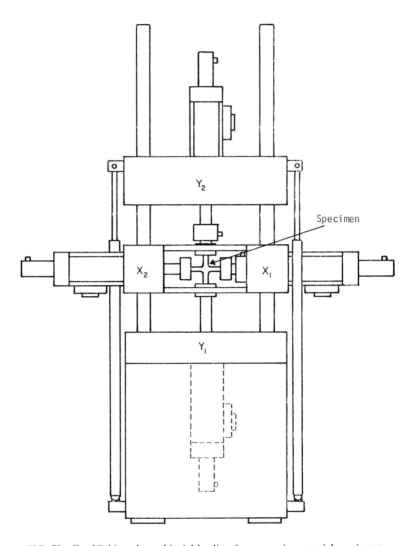

FIG. 50—*Establishing planar biaxial loading for composite material specimens.*

5.2 Tension/Torsion Systems

In these systems, various techniques are used to incorporate both axial push/pull loading, and torsion into the specimen. The type of capability is quite important in the testing of composite materials, especially those with asymmetric fiber configurations (Fig. 51).

The force range of tension/torsion systems varies from a few thousand pounds axial force to over 50 000 lb (22 500 kg) axial force. The torsional

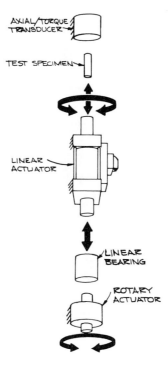

FIG. 51—*An axial torsion test arrangement utilizing a linear bearing to transmit torque through the piston of the linear actuator.*

force has ranged from approximately 2000 lbf·in (226 N·m) to over 20 000 lbf·in (2260 N·m).

There are three different techniques commonly used for coupling the torsional drive system to the axial drive system. The technique selected is determined by the torsional load level and by the application.

A ball spline coupling is used to couple the torsional actuator to the linear actuator for applications when the maximum torque is less than ±5000 lbf·in (565 N·m). It may be possible in some cases to go as high as ±7500 lbf·in (847.5 N·m) with this technique. The ball spline or linear bearing is preloaded to provide zero backlash through zero. The rotary actuator in this case is attached directly to the base.

Torque ratings greater the ±5000 lbf·in (565 N·m) can have the rotary actuator shaft attached directly to the lower end of the linear actuator rod. The rotary actuator is mounted on a bracket that reacts the torsional load into two of the load frame columns through simple bushings. Figure 52 shows an exploded view of the entire drive train.

The third technique is similar to the second, in which the torsional load is reacted through a bracket into the columns, but incorporates a pair of flexures, between the linear and rotary actuators, as shown by the

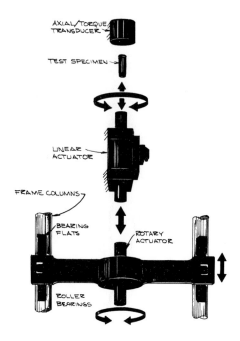

FIG. 52—*A schematic diagram of a tension/torsion fatigue test system.*

exploded view in Fig. 53. The advantage of this technique is that it permits fatigue testing without axial movement of the rotary actuator/ reaction bracket assembly. This, in turn, allows higher frequency testing and reduces wear of the bushings that react the torsional load into the column.

Another configuration is shown in Fig. 54. Here, the rotary and linear actuators are attached to opposite ends of the specimen. This technique requires that the rotary actuator have a thrust bearing that will not only react the axial load, but stand up under fatigue loading. An advantage of such a configuration is that the column length for reacting the torsional load is shorter and keeps overall frame wind-up to a minimum.

A system using this configuration would be preferred for high-frequency applications because of the short column length and absence of large moving masses. The rotary actuator would be mounted on the top of the load frame upper crosshead. A hydrostatic bearing attached to the down side of the crosshead (or as an integral part of the rotary actuator) reacts the axial load. Flexures would be coupled between the linear actuator upper end and reaction bearings attached to two of the vertical columns.

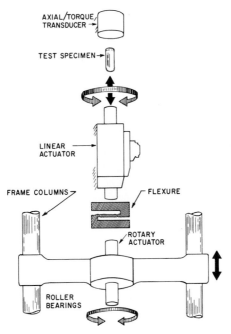

FIG. 53—*A schematic diagram of an axial torsion system utilizing a flexure to transmit torque.*

5.3 Tension/Pressurization

Cyclic internal pressurization of thin-walled tubular specimens will only produce one fixed ratio of the biaxial tensile stresses. In order to investigate the behavior of material under different ratios, superimposed, in-phase, fluctuating axial load can be applied. In such cases, the standard axial loading from a linear actuator forms one loop (with the load applied through threaded ends on the specimen), while a hydraulic pressurization facility sets up a second loop of operation within the system. By selecting the appropriate conditions, biaxial principal stress ratios in the positive and negative regions can be obtained. Since the specimen is in the form of a thin-walled cylinder, the radial stress due to the pressure is relatively small and may be ignored.

The number of investigations carried out has been limited, partly because of the complexity of the testing and control equipment required and partly because of the high cost of test specimens. Fatigue specimens which are to be subjected to internal pressure are usually made with a ground and polished cylindrical inner bore. The outer surface may be prepared similarly and have a parallel or profiled test section.

An alternative method has been used which does not require a separate fluctuating axial load system. Various ratios of tangential to longitudinal

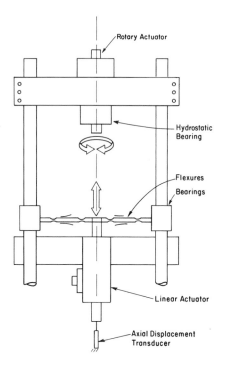

FIG. 54—*An axial stroke torsion fatigue test system, using flexures to react the torsion loads.*

stress are obtained by attaching suitably designed heads to the upper threaded ends of tubular test specimens. A central plug inside the specimen serves to reduce the oil volume in order to allow the pump to develop the required pressure. The desired ratios are obtained essentially by selecting the proper areas in the upper head over which the oil pressure acts relative to the cross-sectional bore areas of the tubes, and attaching the central axial plug within the tube to carry tension or thrust as the case may be.

A more complicated system for biaxial fatigue tests with zero mean stresses utilizes external as well as internal pressurization, the tubular specimen being mounted within a pressure chamber. Reversed axial loading is applied by means of a standard fatigue machine, while the tubular specimen is alternately pressurized inside and outside during each half-cycle. Stress ratios are changed by the use of specimens of different size and by the reversal of the pressure connections.

5.4 Bending/Torsion

Tests under combined bending and torsion have been made in fatigue machines specially designed for the purpose and in standard plane bending or torsion machines with appropriate modifications. In the former case, a vibrating arm is attached through a pivoted joint to one end of the clamped specimen, and this arm can be operated in any angular position with reference to the longitudinal axis of the specimen. In this manner, bending, torsion, and any combination of in-phase bending and torsional stresses may be obtained, since they are dependent upon the angular position of the arm. The arm is excited by a rotating out-of-balance disk, suspended from a long cantilever spring support to which it is connected by a vertical link. The disk is driven at the resonant frequency of the system, and square-ended specimens with a round, profiled test section have been largely employed.

Repeated bending machines of the non-resonant design are generally cantilever loaded. As in the case of cantilever rotating beam machines, the bending moment varies linearly with respect to the distance from the applied load, a transfer shear load is present and a stress gradient occurs with respect to specimen thickness. By offsetting the applied load with respect to the specimen centerline, these machines can be adapted to apply combined bending and torsion. This modification has been used successfully on plate bending machines of the constant deflection type, and tests were made with mean stresses other than zero.

5.5 Triaxial Stress

While studies of fatigue under triaxial stress are relatively few in number, there are two areas in which specialized equipment was used and which may be worth noting. The first of these areas relates to the practical case of thick cylinders or pressure vessels subjected to repeated internal pressure. The stresses developed in such cylinders, when supporting their own end load, can be considered as a uniform triaxial tensile stress acting throughout the wall thickness with a superimposed shear stress which varies from a minimum at the outside to a maximum at the bore. The ratio of the triaxial tension to the shear stress changes with the ratio of the external to internal diameters of the cylinder. The method used to produce the repeated pressure consists of reciprocating a ram in a closed cylinder filled with oil, the pressure being produced by compression of the oil. Tests have been made on relatively small specimens with diameter ratios up to 3:1 and pressures up to 40 000 psi (28 kg/mm²).

The equipment just described was subsequently modified to enable an investigation of the influence of the intermediate principal stress to be carried out. The modification permitted pulsating in-phase tension or compression to be superimposed, utilizing the pulsating oil pressure from the basic system.

In the second area, a system has been devised and used for triaxial tension tests on cubic specimens with six threaded ends in three normal directions. Equal loads are produced simultaneously along each axis by the action of six pistons mounted on the threaded ends and moved outward by oil pressure in a hollow steel block.

Bibliography

Blaser, R. U., Tucker, J. T., and Kooistra, L. F., *Welding Journal,* Vol. 31, March 1952, p. 161-s.

Blass, J. J. and Findley, W. N., *Materials Research and Standards,* Vol. 7, June 1967, p. 254.

Bowman, C, E, and Dolan, T. J., *Welding Journal,* Vol. 32, Nov. 1953, p. 529-s.

Bundy, R. W. and Marin, J., "Fatigue Strength of 14S-T4 Aluminum Alloy Subjected to Baxial Stresses," *Proceedings,* American Society for Testing and Materials, Vol. 54, 1954.

Findley, W. N., "Fatigue of 76S-T61 Aluminum Alloy under Combined Bending and Torsion," ASTM Preprint 57, American Society for Testing and Materials, June 1952.

Findley, W. N. in *Transactions,* American Society of Mechanical Engineers, Vol. 79, 1957, p. 1337.

Gough, H. J., Pollard, H. V., and Clenshaw, W. J., "The Resistance of Metals to Fatigue under Combined Stress," Aeronautical Research Council, Reports and Memoranda, 2522, 1951.

Havard, D. G., *Ontario Hydro Research Quarterly,* Vol. 20, 1st Qtr., p. 14.

Kibler, J. J. and Roberts, R., *Transactions,* American Society of Mechanical Engineers, Vol. 92B, Nov. 1970, p. 727.

McClaren, S. W. and Terry, E. L., "Characteristics of Aerospace Materials Subjected to Biaxial Static and Fatigue Loading Conditions," Paper 63-WA-315, American Society of Mechanical Engineers, 1963.

Majors, H., Mills, B. D., and MacGregor, C. W., *Journal of Applied Mechanics,* Vol. 16, 1949, p. 269.

Marin, J., *Journal of Applied Mechanics,* Vol. 16, 1949, p. 383.

Morrison, J. L. M., Crossland, B., and Parry, J. S. C. in *Proceedings,* Institution of Mechanical Engineers, Vol. 170, 1965, p. 697.

Pascoe, K. J. and de Villiers, J. W. R., *Journal of Strain Analysis,* Vol. 2, April 1967, p. 117.

Rotvel, F., "Biaxial Fatigue Tests with Zero Mean Stresses Using Tubular Specimens," Dept. of Applied Mechanics, Techn. University of Denmark, Copenhagen, Oct. 1969.

Swanson, S. R., *Test Engineering Magazine,* May 1971, p. 1.

Topper, T. H., Havard, D. G., Gowda, C. V. B., and Jhansale, H. R., *Journal of Materials,* Dec. 1971, p. 842.

Welter, G. and Choquet, J. A., *Welding Journal,* Vol. 42, Dec. 1963, p. 565-s.

Wilson, I. H. and White, D. J., *Journal of Strain Analysis,* Vol. 6, Jan. 1971, p. 27.

Chapter 6—Specimens for Material Fatigue Testing

The specimens to be described are intended primarily for the determination and comparison of the basic fatigue characteristics of different materials and for studies of the effect of notches, surface finish, environment, and such surface treatments as plating, carburizing, and shot-peening. The testing of actual components and structures is discussed in Chapter 10.

6.1 Specimen Design

A specimen is a representative sample of the material under investigation and should be the embodiment of the question the engineer is asking of the material. It consists essentially of three parts: the center or test section, which is the region where the required test conditions are simulated as closely as possible, and the two ends, which serve only to transfer the load from the grips into the center section. Since the center section is the region under study, its cross-section whether cylindrical or flat (rectangular) is generally reduced so that this area is more highly stressed than the gripping portions and failure in the grips is thereby avoided. The transition from the test section to the ends should be made smoothly by generous fillets in order to minimize the stress raising effects.

The type of specimen used will depend upon the objective of the investigation, the fatigue testing equipment available and its capacity, and the form of the material. Two general criteria for the design have already been mentioned, namely, that failure should occur in the test section and that unintentional stress raisers should be avoided. In addition, it is desirable that the dimensions of the section should be such that the loads required are not disproportionately low with respect to the capacity of the machine, and that the natural frequency of the specimen is well removed from that of the machine. The stiffness or spring rate of the specimen is also important, since it will affect the dynamic response of the system of which it forms a part. Stiffness limitations will depend upon the system or machine being used and are normally provided by the manufacturer.

If the objective of the investigation is to study the notch sensitivity of a material under cyclic loading, the specimen design will necessarily incorporate some form of geometric stress raiser, for example, a V-notch or sharp fillet. In such cases, reduction of the cross-sectional dimensions of the center portion is usually unnecessary unless dictated by the load capacity of the fatigue machine. Maximum stresses in a notched specimen may be determined by calculating nominal stresses in the same way as for unnotched specimens and correcting these values by means of a stress concentration factor, K_t. This factor has been determined theoretically and experimentally for various types of notches and fillets of comparatively simple shapes.

Specimens are often inadequately specified in fatigue investigations. An engineering drawing is essential and should show the shape, size, and dimensions of the specimen, together with the tolerances. It should include details of the test section, the gripping sections, the transition fillets, and the notch, if required. Restrictions on the degree of out-of-straightness of the specimen and lack of concentricity (round specimens) should be provided. If the specimen contains a notch, the corresponding stress concentration factor and its method of derivation should be noted. In addition, the orientation of the specimen with respect to the direction of maximum working of the material should be indicated in the specification.

A typical specimen for rotating beam tests is shown in Fig. 55. Note the tolerances, the details for polishing, and the generally high quality of preparation implied in the drawing.

6.1.1 Axially-Loaded Specimens

The general criteria mentioned in the foregoing apply equally to both round and flat specimens for axial-load tests. Specimens with circular cross-sections may be either of two types—those with tangentially blending fillets between the center section and the ends, and those with a continuous radius between the ends. In the former case, it is recommended that the transition radius should be at least 8 times the test section diameter, and the test section length should be greater than 3 times its diameter. For tests run in compression, the test section length should be less than 4 times its diameter to minimize buckling, unless provisions are made to support the specimen without affecting the loads applied to the test section by more than 5 percent. In the latter case, the radius of curvature should be no less than 8 times the minimum diameter of the test section. Recommendations for the length of the test section are the same.

Specimens with rectangular cross-sections may have a reduced test section in one dimension only, generally the width, or they may require dimensional reductions in both width and thickness. Such specimens, also, may be either of two types—those with tangentially blending fillets between the uniform test section and the ends, and those with a continuous radius between the ends. In the former case, it is recommended that the transition radius should be at least 8 times the

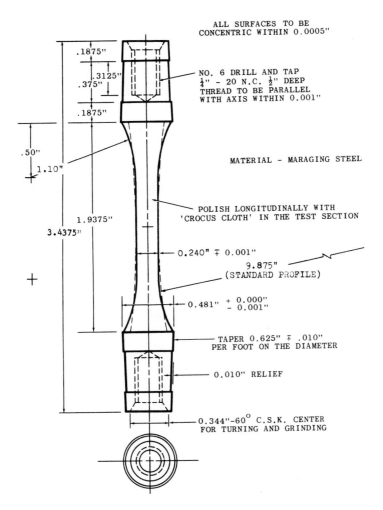

FIG. 55—*Typical specimen for rotating beam tests.*

specimen width, and the ratio of width to thickness in the test section should be between 2 and 6. Restrictions on test section length in terms of its width are similar to those just given, with the proviso that lateral specimen support must be incorporated for compression tests on thicknesses less than 0.100 in. (2.54 mm). In the latter case, the recommendations are the same as those for waisted cylindrical specimens, with the substitution of width for diameter.

The design of the enlarged ends of the specimen for gripping purposes will naturally depend upon the form of the material and the grips available for the particular fatigue machine, but it is recommended that the area of the grip section should be at least 2 times that of the test section. For round specimens, threaded ends are normally used although tests have been made with button-head ends and with straight cylindrical ends. Special precautions are necessary if the cyclic loading passes through zero.

Flat specimens may be tested using wedge-type grips, but are more frequently designed for some form of pin loading. The diameter of the pin hole is normally of the order of $W/3$, where W is the width of the gripping portion, but the following design considerations should be observed if shear or bearing failures at the pin holes are to be avoided.

Shear failure—The pin holes are so located with respect to the ends of the test specimen as to avoid shearing of the metal between the pin hole and the end of the specimen. If the distance between the center of the hole and the end of the specimen (e) is from 1½ to 2 times the diameter of the hole (D)

$$e/D > 1.5$$

failure is unlikely to occur in shear.

Bearing failure—compression of the metal at the hole by the bearing pressure between the cylindrical surface of the pin and the hole edge is another cause of specimen failure. The bearing stress is calculated from the following expression

$$S_b = P_{max}/tD$$

where P_{max} is the maximum tensile load that will be applied to the test specimen, t is the specimen thickness at the hole, and D is the diameter of the hole. To avoid deformation at the pin holes, the design limit should be

$$S_{by} > P_{max}/tD$$

where S_{by} is the bearing yield strength of the metal. Published values of S_{by} are usually reported as a function of e/D, and may be found in MIL-HDBK-5.

Typical grips used in fatigue tests of conventional specimens are shown in Fig. 56. If the form of the material, however, is such that the test section cannot be reduced, for example, wire, the problem of preventing failure in the grips must be handled differently. Special grips are commercially available with jaws which contain multiple slits perpendicular to the loading direction. The spacing between the slits changes from one end of the jaws to the other, so that the specimen is held by many clamps in parallel, the most flexible clamps being near the test section. Alternatively, with many materials it is possible to increase the fatigue strength of the grip portion of the wire by shot-peening or rolling so that

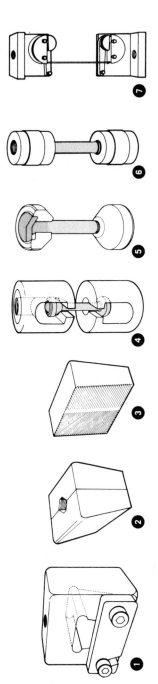

1. Standard grip body for wedge-type grips.
2. Vee grips for rounds for use in standard grip body. Set of four.
3. Flat grips for specimens for use in standard grip body.
4. Universal open front holders.
5. Adapters for special samples, that is, screws, bolts, studs, etc., for use with universal open front holders.
6. Holders for threaded samples.
7. Snubber-type wire grips for flexible wire or cable.

FIG. 56—*Grips used in fatigue testing.*

failure occurs outside this region. It is worth noting that these procedures can frequently be used successfully to strengthen the gripping ends of specimens which have been underdesigned or incorrectly machined.

Intentional geometric stress concentrations may be produced in a specimen of circular test section by means of fillets, transverse holes, and circumferential grooves. Other types of stress raisers such as threads, keyways, splines, etc., will be regarded as belonging to components. The geometry of fillets, and hence the K_t value, is defined by the major and minor diameters and the transition fillet radius, and that of transverse holes by the diameters of the test section and the hole. The geometry of a circumferential V-notch is defined by the major and minor diameters, the radius at the root of the notch and the flank angle.

Similarly, stress concentrations are produced in flat specimens by means of fillets, holes, and edge notches. The hole type notch may be varied not only by changing the ratio of the hole diameter to the width of the specimen but also by locating the hole at different distances from the edges or by elongating the hole in the longitudinal or transverse direction, or by providing the specimen with two or more holes. The most common types of edge-cut notches are the V and U types.

6.1.2 Bending Specimens

Bending specimens may be round or flat and may be tested under plane bending or rotating bending conditions, although rotating bending specimens are almost invariably round whereas plane bending specimens are usually flat. Furthermore, the specimens may be tested as beams or cantilevers, and the test section may be subjected to a uniform or varying bending moment. However, the general considerations outlined before apply equally to bending specimens and there are many points of similarity with axially loaded specimens.

Rotating bending specimens may contain a parallel length with tangentially blending fillets at the ends or may have a continuous radius. Typical examples of each type are shown in Fig. 55. As in the case of the axially-loaded specimens, it is desirable to keep the transition radii or the continuous radius as large as practicable in order to minimize stress concentration effects. The design of the gripping ends of the specimen will depend upon the type of machine being used. The ends may be relatively short and tapered, with internal threads, as shown for the symmetrical rotating beam specimen, or they may be longer and parallel, as for an unsymmetrical cantilever specimen. In the latter case, one end is gripped in a collet chuck, while load is applied through a bearing mounted in the other end.

Cantilever, plane-bending specimens of sheet and plate vary considerably in dimensions, but generally follow one of two basic designs. The first is shaped so that each side of the reduced section is formed by a single circular arc. In the second type of design, the reduced section has straight tapered sides. If the taper is such that the extensions of the sides intersect in the centerline of the crank pin through which load is applied, the bending stress will be constant over the fillets, hence, care should be taken to use as large a fillet as possible and to ensure that there is no discontinuity where the fillets and straight sides meet. Similar considerations apply to beam-type bending specimens, which may have tangential blending fillets or one continuous radius between the enlarged ends. In each case, the design of the gripping portions is dictated by the clamping arrangement of the particular machine, and generally presents no problems.

Intentional geometric stress raisers may be produced in round or flat specimens in the same manner as for the corresponding axially loaded specimens, and the comments in the appropriate paragraphs of Section 6.1.1 apply similarly to bending specimens.

6.1.3. Torsion Specimens

Torsion fatigue tests are normally carried out on round specimens and the design of the specimens is basically the same as that of cylindrical rotating bending specimens. The essential difference lies in the method used for gripping the specimens which may involve a keyway or flattened portions on the cylindrical ends, depending upon the particular machine. The general considerations just mentioned regarding the proportioning of the specimens, the size of the transition or continuous radius, and the introduction of stress raisers apply equally to torsion specimens.

6.2 Specimen Preparation

Fatigue in a homogeneous material is essentially a surface dependent phenomenon and the great majority of fatigue failures originate at the surface. Too much emphasis, therefore, cannot be placed on the importance of specimen preparation in this respect. One of the principal purposes of specimen-type fatigue testing is the accumulation of useful basic fatigue data which is comparable, reproducible, and capable of correlation between laboratories. In order to attempt to obtain such ideal data with universal meaning, it is essential that uniform specimen preparation procedures be established and practiced, particularly for the test portion of the specimen on which the calculated fatigue stresses are imposed. The procedures should be carefully and rigidly specified for the various stages of rough machining, finish machining, and polishing, and adequate control should be exercised in the machine shop operations. It may even be advisable to inform the machine shop of the importance of the preparation of fatigue specimens as compared to specimens for other mechanical tests, since carelessly prepared specimens may not be replaceable, due to shortage of material, or if undetected, may result in incorrect data and erroneous conclusions.

The influence of the various preparation methods on the fatigue behavior may be radically different for different materials and hardness levels, but there are certain general considerations which should be noted. In the first case, it is necessary to ensure that any shaping or machining operation required does not alter the metallurgical structure or properties of the specimen. For this reason methods involving heat, such as oxygen flame cutting, should not be used, and the cuts taken in machining should not be so deep as to cause work-hardening of the specimen surface. Milling and turning are preferred processes for soft materials, but grinding may be used for the harder steels, providing an adequate supply of coolant is available to prevent overheating of the specimen surface. Cutting tools must be kept sharp and grinding wheels dressed at suitable intervals. Grinding, in particular, should not be too severe, since it may produce microcracks and undesirable residual tensile stresses in the surface layers, even though the measured surface finish appears adequate. The final operation is normally polishing and should be carried out either by hand or by machine, using successively finer grades of emery cloth or paper. The preliminary polishing stages may be alternately longitudinal and circumferential, but the direction of the final stage should always be longitudinal. The finished test section should obviously contain no unintentional stress raisers, such as transverse scratches or poorly-blended transition fillets.

It would be extremely difficult to attempt to establish specimen preparation procedures for all the engineering materials likely to be encountered. An additional complication is the fact that the procedure will vary with the objective of the investigation. The requirements for a fundamental study on single crystals of high purity aluminum will be vastly different from those for a comparison of two commercial steels. However, since no ASTM standards for fatigue specimen preparation are available at the present time, some recommended practices used for steel and aluminum, which may serve as guides for other materials where appropriate, will be described.

6.2.1 Machining the Specimen

6.2.1.1 Round Specimens—When machining round specimens, there are three main effects which should be avoided: (1) overheating the specimen during machining, (2) cold working the material at the surface of the specimen, and (3) repeatedly stressing the specimen during the machining by excessive vibration. The order of machining operations is sometimes important. When specimens are prepared on a lathe, it is suggested that the test section of the specimen be machined last and that the feed be toward the head stock in order to minimize the chances of repeatedly stressing the material in the test section of small specimens. If the specimens are stress relieved or otherwise heat treated after machining, care should be exercised to avoid such defects as decarburization and oxidation, unless these are the variables under test.

Test specimens for rotating-beam machines must be prepared very carefully to ensure that the grip ends are accurate and the axis at one end coincides with the axis at the other, so that the specimen will run true in the machine. Care must be exercised in the preparation of specimens for axial-load fatigue tests to ensure that the test section is concentric with the grip ends of the specimen. Otherwise, appreciable bending stresses may be introduced due to eccentric loading.

The machining procedure outlined in the following is directly applicable to rotating-beam fatigue specimens (Fig. 55), but can be adapted to any other cylindrical specimen.

1. Cut piece to exact length and turn to 1/2 in. (12.7 mm) diameter on centers.
2. Re-center with controlled depth; drill and tap both ends.
3. Stencil identification on both ends.
4. Heat treat if required.
5. Rough turn or grind, depending upon the strength level, to 0.025 in. (0.65 mm) oversize.
6. Finish turn or grind center section to 0.008 in. (0.20 mm) oversize.
7. Finish grind center section to +0.002 in. (0.05 mm) or +0.003 in. (0.075 mm) oversize; depth of cut not to exceed 0.001 in. (0.025 mm).
8. Grind tapers.

The foregoing procedure is generally applied to the preparation of ferrous metal specimens. The machining procedure for cylindrical aluminum alloy specimens is a relatively simple process, and usually consists of turning operations in a lathe. The depth of the initial cuts may be up to 0.050 in. (1.25 mm), but the finishing cuts should be of the order of 0.020 in. (0.5 mm), 0.003 in. (0.075 mm), and 0.002 in. (0.05 mm), respectively.

Specimens made of other soft nonferrous materials should follow the same general procedure as for aluminum. In fabricating fatigue specimens made of titanium, the machining procedure outlined for ferrous metal specimens, in general, should be followed.

For the further guidance and information of the reader, similar general procedures for specimen preparation are recommended by the ISO and by the British Standards Institution, and an extract from the latter is quoted here:

> *b. Turning.* It is recommended that the following procedures should be adopted:
>
> (i) In rough turning the test piece from a diameter $x + 0.2$ in. ($x + 5$ mm) (x will generally be the diameter, d, plus a suitable allowance for surface finishing) to $x + 0.2$ in. ($x + 0.5$ mm), the sequence and the depth of cuts should be
>
> 0.05 in. (1.25 mm), 0.03 in. (0.75 mm) and 0.01 in. (0.25 mm).
>
> (ii) From a diameter of $x + 0.02$ in. ($x + 0.5$ mm) to x, the sequence and the depth of cuts should be
>
> 0.005 in. (0.125 mm), 0.003 in. (0.075 mm) and 0.002 in. (0.05 mm), using for these finishing cuts a feed not exceeding 0.025 in. (0.06 mm) per revolution.
>
> *c. Grinding.* For test pieces in material which cannot be readily turned, it is recommended that the finishing operations are carried out by grinding. Where the strength properties of the material are developed in heat treatment may be carried out after rough turning to a diameter of $x + 0.02$ in. ($x + 0.5$ mm).
>
> Test pieces should then be ground to size in the following manner:
>
> 0.001 in. (0.025 mm) depth of cut of 0.04 in. (0.1 mm) oversize;
> 0.0002 in. (0.005 mm) depth of cut to 0.001 in. (0.025 mm) oversize;
> 0.0001 in. (0.0025 mm) depth of cut to size.

6.2.1.2 Flat Specimens—For descriptive purposes, the term "face" of a flat specimen refers to the front and back surfaces which are frequently those of the original sheet of material. The surfaces at right angles to the faces are called the sides of the specimen, and the intersection of a face and a side will be termed an edge.

The majority of flat specimens are machined from sheet or thin extrusions and tested with the as-fabricated surface intact. Machining, which in these cases is limited to the edges, is generally accomplished by milling longitudinally although cross milling is also utilized. In cases where the flat surfaces are machined, machining should be longitudinal. A shaper can be used for the operation, provided that the tool is sharp and well rounded.

Subject to the overriding precautions mentioned in Section 6.2.1.1, the machining procedure outlined in the following is directly applicable to the repeated bending flat plate specimen made from sheet material, but can be adapted to any other type of flat specimen of either sheet or plate.

1. Identify the specimen with the long dimension either parallel or transverse to the direction of rolling, since fatigue characteristics of most materials are directional, and cut or shear to oversize blanks.
2. Mounting holes, if required, are drilled with a jig.
3. Stack the drilled blanks in groups of ten or fifteen, depending upon thickness, and gang machine the sides in the longitudinal direction on a milling machine, with proper size milling cutters, feeds, and speeds appropriate for the material. Use successively lighter cuts with the last two or three cuts removing about 0.0005 in. (0.0125 mm).
4. Remove sharp edges by breaking them by hand to an approximate radius of 0.005 in. (0.125 mm), using a fine No. 500 emery paper moving in the longitudinal direction in order to leave no harmful scratches.

6.2.1.3. Notched Specimens—The machining procedure to be followed in preparing cylindrical U- or V-notched fatigue specimens, except for the notch itself, is similar to that recommended for unnotched specimens. The notch is then rough machined or ground, depending upon the strength level; with the cutting device advancing perpendicular to the specimen axis, to 0.015 in. (0.38 mm) to 0.020 in. (0.50 mm) oversize. Speed and feed vary according to material. Shape and dimensions of the notch are measured by an optical comparator. The notch is then ground to an oversize of 0.005 in. (0.125 mm) in the diameter employing feeds not greater than 0.0003 in. (0.0075 mm) per revolution.

Any notches to be machined in specimens of aluminum, magnesium, and similar alloys should be machined about 0.012 in. (0.30 mm) oversize and then machined to final size with a notch-finishing tool that has been carefully ground or lapped or both. Notches in some nonferrous metals similar in properties to high strength steel should be ground under conditions similar to those used for grinding notches in steel specimens.

The machining procedure to be followed in bringing the flat notched fatigue specimen to size, except for the notch itself, is also similar to that recommended for the unnotched specimen, including the breaking of the edges. Each edge notch is individually cut, on opposite sides, either by machining or grinding depending upon the material and its strength level. Recommendations with regard to the roughing cuts and the finishing cuts or grinding operation are essentially the same as those for notched cylindrical specimens. The comments concerning aluminum, magnesium and similar alloys, and certain nonferrous metals also apply.

It should be borne in mind that notched specimens are so designed that failure will occur at the notched cross-section. The surface preparation of the remainder of the test section is therefore not as important as in the case of unnotched specimens.

6.2.2. Polishing the Specimen

It should be remembered that polishing is a cutting and not a buffing or smearing operation, and that the objective is to remove the scratches caused by machining or grinding. Generally, any method which produces a uniform reproducible surface without cold working, imposing residual stress, overheating, or otherwise altering the material structure will constitute good polishing procedure. Experience has shown that complicated polishing procedures are no more effective in obtaining fatigue values that are in agreement, than is a uniform standard finish, not necessarily highly polished.

Many polishing methods in use are designed to produce a specific smoothness. Roughness limits as low as 2 μin. (0.05 μm) and as high as 32 μin. rms (0.8 μm) are specified. One should realize, however, that obtaining a certain smoothness does not ensure that the surface treatment has produced a minimum of cold work and residual stress.

Both notched and unnotched aluminum specimens are frequently not polished, but are left with a final machined surface. For most nonferrous specimens a machined surface is often more desirable than a polished surface because (1) it is more easily produced, (2) it represents a practical condition, and (3) it has extremely mild stress raisers if machined carefully with a round tool.

The polishing operation normally involves the use of successively finer grades of abrasive papers or cloths. The polishing should generally be in the longitudinal direction, although intermediate stages may be done in any direction to ensure that longitudinal scratches made by the coarser grades of abrasive papers or cloths are removed. The direction of the final polishing stage, however, should always be longitudinal.

6.2.2.1 Round Specimens—There are commercially available automatic polishing machines for round specimens which are a good investment for fatigue testing laboratories anticipating a significant amount of unnotched material fatigue testing. These devices provide a high degree of repeatability in quality, and can perform the awkward longitudinal polishing with ease.

Alternatively, the investigator may prefer to design his own polishing equipment, bearing in mind the principles discussed in Section 6.2.2.

6.2.2.2 Flat Specimens—The surfaces of flat specimens are generally left unpolished, but the sharp edges should be broken (as described in Section 6.2.1.2 on machining) and the sides polished longitudinally to a surface finish of 5 μin. (0.125 μm) rms. In the event that surface polishing is considered to be desirable, electro-polishing may be preferable to mechanical polishing. The details of the electro-polishing procedure will vary with the material being treated, but the method is compatible with the requirements mentioned earlier for satisfactory polishing and it is readily adaptable to a variety of specimen shapes. Some preliminary experimentation is usually necessary to develop the optimum conditions. In this respect, it should be noted that electro-polishing can introduce residual tensile stresses, and can produce surface pitting or differential etching or both, if carelessly carried out.

6.2.2.3. Notched Specimens—U- and V-Notches may be polished by means of a rotating member immersed in an abrasive. Two or more successively finer grades of abrasive slurry are used, for example, 280 grit in SAE 30 oil and 3F grit in SAE 30 oil. Round specimens are mechanically rotated while a taut string immersed in a slurry is rotated in the notch. Flat specimens are held stationary while a soft metal rod or wire, painted with a slurry, is rotated in the notch.

In the case of notched specimens, the reader is reminded that the finish of the test section, other than the notch, is of less importance, unless the stress concentration factor of the notch is quite low, since fracture will occur at the notch. Polishing of the remainder of the test section is, therefore, unnecessary.

6.2.3. Specimens for Surface Treatment Studies

The surface preparation methods just discussed are intended primarily for investigations of the basic fatigue characteristics of the materials involved and for studies of its notch sensitivity under cyclic loading. Information is often required, however, regarding the effect on these characteristics of various surface treatments to be used for specific service applications, for example, carburizing, nitriding, and electro-plating.

The importance of the surface layers in fatigue specimens has already been stressed, and changes in the chemical composition and micro-structure of these layers can result in significant changes in the fatigue strength of the specimens. Two factors are usually responsible for the resultant effects: (1) the change in the fatigue strength of the surface layers which may retard or accelerate crack initiation, and (2) the introduction of residual stresses which may be harmful or beneficial.

Generally, it is desirable to prepare the treated specimens in the same manner with regard to machining and polishing as the untreated control specimens, in order to obtain an effective comparison. This will depend, however, upon the objective of the investigation.

Some common surface treatment processes which produce changes in the chemical composition of the surface layers of a specimen are briefly summarized in the following to emphasize their possible effects on fatigue behavior.

(a) Carburizing—The diffusion of carbon atoms into the surface layers of a steel specimen, by heating it in contact with a carbonaceous material, introduces beneficial compressive stresses, and increases the hardness.

(b) Nitriding—The absorption of nitrogen atoms in the surface layers of a steel specimen, by heating it in an atmosphere of ammonia, has similar effects to those of carburizing.

(c) Decarburization—The loss of carbon from the surface of a steel specimen, due, for example, to heat treatment in an oxidizing atmosphere, leads to the development of harmful tensile stresses in the decarburized layer, increased surface roughness and lower mechanical properties.

(d) Plating and Other Surface Coatings—It is well to note that residual stresses in the surface created by electro-plating and other coating processes have the same important effect on the fatigue behavior as those created by other means.

6.3 Pre-Test Specimen Treatment

This section deals with those operations related to the specimen which must be carried out subsequent to its preparation and prior to the commencement of the test.

6.3.1. Specimen Inspection and Measurement

When the specimen has been received in its finished condition from the machine shop, it should first be inspected visually and then measured. A simple step in the inspection procedure, but one that is often overlooked, is to check that the specimen conforms to the engineering drawing and, in particular, that it fits the grips for which it was designed. Visual inspection of the surface of the test section should be carried out at approximately X20. Transverse cracks or machining marks visible at this magnification shall not be acceptable. They may, of course, be removable with an insignificant reduction in the dimensions of the test section. Fluorescent dye penetrant, magnetic particle, or ultrasonic inspection methods may be employed when non-injurious to the specimen.

The dimensions of the test section of the specimen must be determined accurately before the loading required to produce a given stress or strain can be calculated. For specimens with cross sections which are nominally circular, two mutually perpendicular diameters should be measured with enough readings on each to provide a reliable average.

If a micrometer is used, it should be equipped with ball contact points with radii less than the radius of the curved surface to be measured. A thread micrometer with conical contact points may be used for measuring notched specimens. Special care should be taken, however, to avoid a burnishing action, denting, or scratching when the points of the micrometer contact the specimen.

When measuring materials which exhibit a low modulus of elasticity, the contact pressure exerted when tightening the micrometer must be minimized to avoid changing the dimension to be measured.

Potential problems from contact pressure and surface damage resulting from contact with the micrometer may be avoided by use of optical comparators or traveling microscopes instead of mechanical measuring devices. These instruments are particularly recommended for notched specimens, since they enable the geometry of the notch to be checked at the same time.

When using fatigue testing machines in which the axial position of the critical section influences the critical stresses imposed, as in cantilever type machines, care should be used to ensure that the length of the specimen and the distance from the critical section to the end are maintained the same for each specimen.

For rectangular specimens, both the width and thickness at the critical section should be measured. If the width is large enough, measurements of the thickness should be made at various positions across the width to reveal any appreciable nonuniformity of thickness. Unless there is valid justification for doing otherwise, the average value of the thickness should then be used in calculations.

6.3.2. Specimen Storage

There is usually an appreciable interval of time between the manufacture of a specimen and its fatigue test. There will often be a marked difference in the period of time between the manufacture of the first specimen in a test series and its test, and the interval for the last supposedly identical specimen to be tested. For many materials, these variations in storage time can affect the final test results. This is due to the degradation of the specimen surface (corrosion) if left exposed to the environment.

Unfortunately, there is a wide spectrum in the degree of sensitivity to the environment among materials, just as there is also a wide variation in the storage environments. In the extreme cases it is easy to specify storage requirements such as the following:

"Storage before testing shall be in an inert medium, such as dry argon or oil. All traces of the storage medium shall be removed before testing. Damaged specimens shall not be tested."

However, there are many "borderline" cases where the test engineer must judge the suitability of imposing special protection—in storage measures—during the test program.

In contrast to the deleterious effects of corrosive environments, the fatigue strength of many materials is increased by protective chemical coatings or testing in so-called inert atmospheres. Organic oils and greases usually are found to have this effect, particularly those that tend to form tightly adherent surface films. Solid films of materials such as rubber cement also give improved fatigue resistance. These effects emphasize the importance of maintaining surface conditions constant during fatigue testing and the desirability in some cases of duplicating service conditions in the laboratory to obtain accurate estimates of service performance.

Generally, the storage in a clean air-conditioned laboratory of practical materials presents no problem. For other situations, preliminary experimentation may be necessary to permit a sound decision to be made in this area.

In simultaneous corrosion and fatigue, two factors affect the performance of the metal. One is cycle-dependent, and the other is time-dependent. Thus, special care must be exercised in evaluating the effectiveness of different corrosion resistant coatings. If, for instance, specimens coated with two different materials are tested at the same stress and frequency, and fail after different lengths of time t, it is not clear whether it is the duration of time t or number of cycles N or both, which are important. It might be that the short time failure was largely due to fatigue and the long time failure largely due to corrosion.

One approach to this problem is as follows. Adjust the stress level of a group of samples for each coating so that the mean log N for tests of each group is about the same and use the same frequency for all tests. Then the comparison of the effectiveness of the coatings may be based on the comparative fatigue strengths for the two groups. The influence of time duration may be determined by testing other groups at another frequency and stress such that the mean log N is the same as the first groups. The time will then be different but the number of cycles is the same. Thus, a comparison of the fatigue strengths at the same N, but different frequency, shows the effect of time duration.

6.3.3. Specimen Data Record

In the foregoing sections, information has been provided on the factors governing the design and preparation of specimens for material fatigue testing, and suitable methods for their preparation for various types of loading conditions have been presented. The importance of adhering to a satisfactory preparation procedure, once established, has also been stressed. It may be helpful at this point to recapitulate the data regarding the specimen which should be recorded by the investigator. The recording of this data serves two useful purposes. In the first place, it provides basic information for a subsequent report on the findings of the investigation, and its inclusion therein will greatly facilitate the making of comparisons and of engineering judgements for possible service applications. In the second place, it will enable the investigator to check or extend the work at some future date.

A list of the basic information concerning the specimen which it is recommended should be recorded is given in the following.

(a) Details of the material as supplied—specification or designation, form of product (plate, bar, etc.), heat number, melting practice, mechanical working and heat treatment schedule, chemical composition, surface condition, and cleanliness.

(b) Details of the material in the specimen—ultimate tensile strength, yield point or yield strength at a specified offset, elongation, reduction of area, hardness, grain size, and microstructure: the notched tensile strength should be included if notched fatigue tests are involved.

(c) Details of the specimen design—a drawing showing the shape, size, and dimensions of the specimen, including details of the test section, gripping section, transition fillets, etc.: the orientation of the specimen with respect to the direction of maximum working of the material should be indicated. If notched specimens are involved, include the geometry of the notch, its dimensions and stress concentration factor, and the method of derivation of the stress concentration factor.

(d) Details of specimen preparation—machining procedure (method, feed, speed, depth of cuts, coolant and cutting tool sharpening, or dressing interval), polishing technique (grit size, sequence, and direction), thermal treatment (stress relieving, aging, etc.), surface treatment (carburizing, nitriding, peening, etc.), and surface residual stresses, if measured. The chronological order of these operations should be indicated.

(e) Details of pre-test specimen treatment—surface roughness measurements, specimen measuring method, protective coating and storage environment, and method used to remove the protection.

6.4 Special Problems—Heat Generation

Conditions which minimize the rise of temperature of the specimen due to heat generation during cycling are: reduction in size of the specimen, distribution of stress in such a way that only a small proportion of the total specimen volume is at the peak stress, low cycling rates, large ratio of surface area to volume of material at peak stress, high conductivity, good heat transfer characteristics of connections between specimen and machine and of machine itself, artificial removal of heat from the specimen through a forced flow of air or other fluid coolant passing continuously over specimen. It is important that the cooling fluid does not alter the material behavior by some chemical action such as corrosion, solvent action, absorption into the material, or by influencing removal of volatile constituents of the materials.

6.5 Final Remarks

Probably the two most common errors in specimen preparation are:

(a) Undercutting in fillet machining. Often, the machinist is not aware of the profound effect on fatigue life a careless matching of the fillet with the center section will have.

(b) Undue surface working during machining. This is so often a problem that the turning procedure should be completely specified with regard to sequence, tool sharpness, tool setting, speeds, and feeds, so that the final machining is as "gentle" as possible.

Bibliography

Almen, J. O., *Product Engineering,* June 1951, p. 109.
Cina, B., *Metallurgia,* Vol. 55, Jan. 1957, p. 11.
Dugdale, D. S., *Welding Journal,* Vol. 38, Jan. 1959, p. 45-s.
Finney, J. M., Mann, J. Y., and Simpson, R., *Metallurgia,* Vol. 81, Jan. 1970, p. 11.
George, R. E. and Mantle, J. B., *Materials Research and Standards,* Vol. 2, Dec. 1962, p. 1000.
Marchant, R. H., *Metals and Materials,* Vol. 5, June 1971, p. 206.
"Metallic Materials and Elements for Flight Vehicle Structures," MIL-HDBK-5, Dept. of Defense, Washington, Aug. 1962.
"Methods of Fatigue Testing," Parts 1 to 5, British Standard 3518, British Standards Institution.
Neuber, H., "Theory of Notch Stresses," AEC-tr-4547, June 1961, U.S. Atomic Energy Commission.
Peterson, R. E., *Stress Concentration Design Factors,* Wiley, New York, Nov. 1953.
Roberts, J. G. and Mattson, R. L., *Fatigue Durability of Carburized Steels,* American Society for Metals, 1957, p. 68.
Simkovich, E. A. and Loria, E. A. in *Transactions,* American Society for Metals, Vol. 53, 1961, p. 109.
Stulen, F. B., Cummings, H. N., and Schulte, W. C., *Machine Design,* Vol. 33, 8 June 1961, p. 165.
Sutton, H., *Metal Treatment,* Vol. 2, 1936, p. 89.
Tarasov, L. P., Hyler, W. S., and Letner, H. R. in *Proceedings,* American Society for Testing and Materials, Vol. 57, 1957, p. 601.
Watkinson, J., *Coil Spring Journal,* June 1954, p. 14.
Whelan, J. M. and Griffiths, D. W., *Journal of Materials,* Vol. 5, Sept. 1970, p. 529.

Chapter 7—Accuracy of Fatigue Testing

Precision and accuracy are two concepts of statistical characterization of a process. Precision concerns the spread between the individual measurements in the process, whereas accuracy concerns the deviation of such measurements from an accepted reference level for the property or characteristic measured. An accurate process is also precise, but a precise process is not necessarily accurate. Generally, the index of accuracy will consist of two or more different numbers. Since the concept of accuracy embraces not only the concept of precision, but also the idea of more or less consistent deviation from the reference level (systematic error or bias), it is preferable to describe accuracy by separate values indicating precision and bias. For further information, the reader is referred to the ASTM Recommended Practice for Use of the Terms Precision and Accuracy as Applied to Measurement of a Property of a Material (E 177-71).

In fatigue testing, nearly every parameter involved is subject to some degree of variability. In this chapter, many of these parameters will be discussed, for example, specimen dimensional accuracy, read-out accuracy, control accuracy, programming accuracy, and overall accuracy. The present state of the art in machine verification techniques, alignment, and gripping problems will also be dealt with in detail.

The significance of loading accuracy in fatigue testing can be appreciated by realizing the relation between loading (or straining) level and fatigue life. In either constant or variable amplitude loading, the relation typically involves the load parameter to a multiple of six. For example, a 5 percent error in load amplitude can result in almost a 40 percent error in fatigue life. A given amplitude of load, for example, ±10 000 lb (4500 kg), can be obtained to the nearest pound, that is, ±1 lb (0.45 kg) only if very expensive equipment is used, whereas equipment which performs to the nearest 100 lb (45 kg) will be far more economical. As a result, fatigue testing tends to be conducted within horizontal bands centered at the "nominal" stress level (Fig. 57) [31]. This point becomes very significant when testing near the fatigue limit.

Other sources of variability in test results are change of operator, mechanical wear, changes in testing apparatus, systematic changes in source of specimens, introduction of pollutants in a vacuum fatigue system, etc.

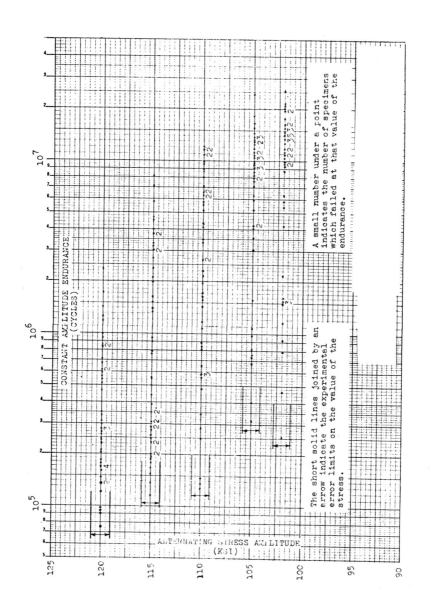

FIG. 57—Plot of alternating stress amplitude versus constant amplitude fatigue endurance.

7.1 Specimen Dimensional Accuracy

In Fatigue testing, specimen dimensions are generally held to a tolerance of ±0.004 in. (0.1 mm), while the dimensions of critical test sections should be held to a tolerance of ±0.001 in. (0.025 mm). Concentricity or axiality of the loading ends or both and the centerline of the specimen should be held to 0.001 in. (0.025 mm) and rotating beam specimens should run true to within 0.005 in. (0.012 mm) total indicator reading. The root radius of a notched dimension should be maintained to ±0.0005 in. (0.012 mm) and ±0.0002 in. (0.005 mm) depending upon the variations of the stress concentration factor with the ratio of the cross-section to the net-section dimension. In general, dimensions used for calculating nominal stress should be measured within an accuracy of ±1 percent, and the nominal stress applied should be calculated on the basis of the actual, not the nominal, dimensions of the specific specimens.

The measurement of specimens to the required accuracy is not as simple a procedure as may appear at first glance. The object of measuring the specimen is to provide data from which to calculate the load, bending moment, or twisting moment needed to produce the desired stresses.

Further analysis of this accuracy problem is given in Ref 32.

7.2 Gripping Effects

In order to ensure axiality of the applied load, machine manufacturers generally specify conditions of concentricity and parallelism of critical machine parts. While this is an essential starting point, it is not sufficient in itself to establish that the specimen to be tested will be subjected to uniformly applied stress across its cross section, since the specimen must be mounted in the machine by some form of gripping device. The conventional methods of gripping specimens in the materials test were indicated in Fig. 56 for round and for flat specimens under axial loading. In both cases, the degree of alignment of the gripping mechanism is largely a function of the care taken in its initial design. Special devices are made up to ensure the concentricity of the axes of the grips, and great attention is paid to locking the grips to faces which are exactly at right-angles to the loading direction.

In addition to the conventional grips, special "self-aligning" grips are available from many fatigue machine manufacturers. In such grip systems, use is frequently made of a temporary fluid connection to permit the specimen itself to align the grips. In one such device, hydraulic fluid not only provides pressure on the gripping wedges, but also seats or unseats the gripping heads against a central spherical shoulder. In another, a low melting point alloy, such as Wood's metal, is used as a temporary fluid coupling between the lower grip on the specimen and the actuator, load cell, or test frame. In the latter case, it should be noted that an error in the top grip will still produce some bending in the specimen.

It is only realistic to assume, however, that it is not consistently possible to have a truly axial load applied to the specimen, and the extent of the non-axiality should therefore be determined.

It is recommended that strain gages be used to measure the bending strains induced in the specimen. Since the specimen configuration is inter-related with the magnitude of bending strain that will be measured by the strain gages, care should be taken to select a strain-gaged specimen that is similar in configuration to the specimens that are to be fatigue tested. The best technique would be to strain gage the actual fatigue test specimen, if possible, provided that the installation of the strain gages will not influence the test results.

Bending is defined as a percentage

$$\text{percent bending} = \frac{\text{maximum strain} - \text{average strain}}{\text{average strain}} \times 100 \text{ percent}$$

The maximum percent bending as defined by this equation should not exceed 5 percent for any given varying stress.

The use of this equation to determine bending percentages assumes that the bending moment is uniform along the length of the test specimen. This is not true in some cases, so care must be taken to ensure that the strain gages are installed in the region of the maximum bending moment.

Four strain gages uniformly spaced around the periphery of the specimen and whose center points lie in a common transverse plane are used to measure bending strains in the case where there is a uniform bending strain. More than one transverse plane must be strain gaged to determine strains when the bending moment is not constant.

In grip alignment, certain adjustments are much more important than others in reducing or eliminating bending stress in the specimen. For example, the pressure exerted in gripping the specimen can easily cause distortions if there is appreciable plastic flow. If a specimen is to be tested in pure tension or compression with an average cyclic stress of S_a. Bending in the specimen will cause a stress, S_b, that locally adds to the average stress and tends to cause premature failure of the specimen.

The possible causes of bending in this specimen are side play in the actuator bearings, angular misalignment between actuator and specimen, initial grip misalignment, and off-center mounting of the specimen on the actuator. Some simple calculations, based on a few assumptions, enable a reasonable assessment to be obtained of the relative magnitude of the bending stress induced.

In a typical actuator, the side play in the bearings would not normally exceed ±0.002 in. (0.050 mm). If the stiffness of the specimen was sufficiently low, the ram end could deflect ±0.0025 in. (0.062 mm) at the normal position in the center of the stroke. For a steel specimen, gripped rigidly at each end, the bending stress resulting from this deflection would be of the order of 100 ksi, which is obviously intolerable. A stiff specimen, however, would not deflect to this extent.

If one assumes an angular misalignment between specimen and ram of 0.001 radians, the following relationship between the bending and applied stresses can be derived for a rigidly mounted specimen.

$$S_b/S_a = 0.004 \frac{L}{d}$$

where

L = specimen gage length, and
d = specimen diameter.

For a specimen with a length to diameter ratio less than 10, the bending stress will be less than 4 percent of the average stress. It will be apparent, therefore, that specimen stiffness is a significant factor as regards stresses due to misalignment and rotation of the line of action of the load with respect to the specimen axis.

Initial grip misalignment is another factor that can cause bending in the specimen. In a machine with wedge grips built into the heads, for example, the initial bending would be dependent upon the precision of the gripping heads and the precision of the alignment between the ram and the upper crosshead. One misalignment configuration of this type is a simple bend with the angle equal at both ends and no lateral displacement. The specimen assumes a curved shape with constant radius, and the induced bending stress is given by

$$S_b = \frac{2EQc}{L}$$

where
E = the modulus of elasticity,
Q = misalignment, radians, and
c = distance from neutral axis to surface.

For an initial misalignment of 0.001 radians and a 2-in. (50.8-mm) long, 0.505-in. (12.8-mm) diameter steel specimen, the bending stress is 7500 psi (5.3 kg/mm²).

This degree of misalignment would be too high in most material testing machines unless some system of specimen alignment were provided. A long slender specimen would, of course, have a lower initial bending moment, but could develop higher bending stresses under load as has been indicated.

7.2.1 Self-Aligning Devices

Some of these problems can be alleviated by the use of special grip alignment devices, such as a self-aligning flexure grip. The so-called flexure or flexure component of such a device would consist of a machined part that is very flexible in bending, but stiff in compression and tension. If the specimen were mounted in the grips at an angle due to grip or specimen inaccuracies, the flexures would be free to bend so that the specimen would remain straight, thus introducing no bending moment. If the specimen were perfectly aligned with the flexure center, no bending stresses could be introduced when a load is applied. However, perfect alignment is virtually impossible and in the practical case some degree of off-center mounting (δ) will occur. An approximate expression for the ratio of bending to applied stress is given by

$$\frac{S_b}{S_a} = \frac{8\delta}{d}$$

The magnitude of δ will depend upon the type of grips and the degree of accuracy used in machining the specimen. A value of 0.005 in. (0.127 mm), which is probably low for wedge grips and slightly high for threaded grips, would give a ratio of 0.08, or 8 percent, for a 0.505-in. (12.7-mm) diameter specimen. In the compression case, the ratio would be somewhat higher, due to the tendency of the specimen to buckle under load and increase the center deflection.

A more frequently used alignment device is the self-aligning spherical seat. It differs from the flexure device in that it utilizes friction to prevent misalignment under load. When a specimen is mounted in the grips, the spherical seats slip to eliminate bending stresses in the no-load condition. When load is applied, the friction in the seats prevents any movement so that, even if the specimen was mounted off center, no bending would be introduced in a straight specimen. Comparing the moment that the spherical seats can support due to friction with that exerted by off-center mounting, it can be shown that the seats will not move if

$$\delta < RC_f$$

where

$R = $ radius of spherical seats, and
$C_f = $ coefficient of friction.

Taking typical values of $R = 3$ in. (76 mm) and $C_f = 0.01$, it is apparent that off-center mounting up to 0.03 in. (0.76 mm) will not induce bending in a specimen.

7.3 Machine Effects

Apart from those factors common to all machines which will be dealt with in subsequent sections, there are certain effects peculiar to individual machines or to specific tests. For example, some machines have starting and stopping transients. A critical speed may be encountered before reaching the operating speed, or for some other reason excessive vibration may be produced in starting up the machine. The starting technique is therefore important. Outside restraint by clamps or by the operator himself may be required, or it may be necessary to delay application of the full test load until the machine is up to operating speed. Machines which are susceptible to such problems on starting should be equipped with some device to prevent automatic restarting after being stopped by some unforeseen event, such as a power failure.

Under some conditions, substantial inelastic behavior during the first few cycles will require adjustment of settings of the machine to maintain conditions intended for the test. Such circumstances may call for cycling by hand with repeated readjustments of controls until no further change is observed. Two words of caution are necessary for such tests. (1) Results should not be expected to agree with those from tests where the machine is allowed to continue for the entire test with initial calculated settings ignoring inelastic action, and, (2) interpretation of the results should include some recognition of the effect of the inelastic behavior.

In addition to the dynamic problems just mentioned, the combinations of speed, stiffness, and mass may result in a dynamic response which is undesirable or even disastrous. The undesirable consequences of any such combination of characteristics may be avoided by altering one or more of these characteristics. The speed of the machine may be varied or the stiffness may be changed by use of a specimen with a different diameter, or the linkage or levers may be redesigned to change the system's mass or its distribution [33].

Vibrations transmitted to or from other equipment in the vicinity of fatigue testing machines should be eliminated or minimized, through the use of suitable mountings. Springs, rubber couplings, and pads of cork or other high damping materials can be used effectively for this purpose.

7.3.1. Alignment

Alignment is important for different reasons in different types of tests. In rotating beam tests, good alignment is important to minimize eccentricity (runout), which causes appreciable dynamic effects resulting from periodic raising and lowering of the dead weights used to apply loads. Sometimes, it is possible to reduce the undesirable dynamic stresses resulting from vibration or misalignment by inserting a spring in the linkage between the specimen and the load in a rotating beam machine. Such springs can be very helpful if selected to have proper characteristics with respect to masses and frequencies involved in the machine.

7.3.2 Verification

The verification of the static and dynamic loads applied by a fatigue machine is carried out by means of calibrating devices which may take many different forms. The frequency and extent of the operation will depend upon the circumstances. For example, in certain very critical tests, verfication may be desirable both before and after the test, but may be restricted to the load range involved. A more usual approach is to verify the equipment before and after a complete program. Further verifications are necessary whenever anything occurs which might affect the accuracy of the test data, (for example, change of test location, change of operator, etc.). Finally, many laboratories have a simple rule to verify their equipment during certain months (for example, twice a year, December and June), as the workload permits.

For fatigue testing there exists a variety of sources for verification procedures which include:

(*a*) government standards,
(*b*) machine manufacturer standards,
(*c*) user standards, and
(*d*) ASTM standards and recommended practices.

Verification procedures drawn up by standards organizations are usually in the form of specifications, which are discussed in detail in Appendix B. The United States National Bureau of Standards has, for example, static accuracy requirements for load cells [34], and often these static accuracies are used to obtain approval for the use of load cells under fatigue conditions. This is not sufficient in many cases, for a variety of reasons.

1. Transients in starting or stopping the test may occur.
2. The frequency response of one of the elements in the test may not be sufficient to impose the required loadings, (or may cause overloadings if the readout system lacks frequency response).
3. There may be inertia effects in the moving parts of the test machine between the dynamometer and the specimen, as mentioned earlier, which cause dynamic loads to differ from static loads, etc.

Calibration devices such as calibration load cells normally have a certain amount of overload capability (10 to 15 percent), although it is extremely unwise to use an overloaded device without a thorough recheck.

Calibration devices themselves are verified using standard methods of verification of such devices (ASTM Verification of Calibration Devices for Verifying Testing Machines (E 74-64)).

The overall verification of many fatigue machines consists of procedures covering static as well as dynamic operating conditions. For static conditions, reference should be made to ASTM Verification of Testing Machines (E 4-64). For dynamic conditions of axial loading, the reader is referred to ASTM Tentative Recommended Practice for Verification of Constant Amplitude Dynamic Loads in an Axial Load Fatigue Testing Machine (E 467-72 T), and Ref 35.

Dynamic verification is required over the entire load and frequency range where fatigue information is desired for each type of specimen to be tested. Such verification is sometimes difficult to accomplish in a single operation. Some laboratories have instrumented calibration specimens representing the extremes in operation of the test system; for example, a stiff stubby specimen, ideal for the high frequency/low amplitude range, and a long flexible specimen with elongations under load at low frequencies equal to the largest displacement range to be used. It is important to check both load and displacement in many dynamic load situations, since both can affect, for instance, the inertia loadings in the moving grips.

The dynamic verification procedure for an axial-load machine should consist of the following principal steps.

1. Obtain the static load-strain (or a quantity proportional to strain) relationship for the dynamometer using a static testing machine or dead weights.
2. Measure the strains in the dynamometer during cyclic loading at each of the desired maximum and minimum loads and test frequencies in the fatigue machine.
3. Convert the measured strains or appropriate instrumentation readings to loads using the static load-strain relationship.

A dynamometer is essentially an elastic calibration device, consisting of an instrumented member having mass, stiffness, and end displacements such that the inertia effects of the specimen, for which the verification of loads is desired, are duplicated within 1 percent. It should be instrumented with a transducer in such a way as to permit a determination of the average strain in the uniform section of the dynamometer and determination of the amount or percent of bending applied to it when it is subjected to an axial load. An acceptable and frequently used transducer consists of not less than four strain gages mounted longitudinally on the uniform section, equally-spaced around the periphery and with provision for reading out the individual and average strains. The associated instrumentation would include a power supply, amplifier, and oscilloscope.

Many oscilloscope techniques for dynamic verification of constant amplitude fatigue loadings have been developed in conjunction with strain-gage specimens or dynamometers. Generally, the direct use of the dynamic signal without a null technique will limit calibration to 3 to 5 percent accuracy. However, with null techniques and the attendant amplification of the residual signal at the extreme values, very good dynamic accuracies can be achieved. The strain gage is a very high response device in most cases (response of about 5 μs) and when the reading is compared with a highly accurate reference voltage, dynamic accuracies can be checked with as little as a fraction of 1 percent (full scale) error to be added to the static error. Typically, a dynamic null-balance verification compares an unknown input signal with a precision reference voltage and displays the highly amplified difference signal on an oscilloscope. Separate circuits are used for the maximum and minimum null points. The output of these two circuits are summed together to form the output signal for the oscilloscope. The minimum circuit provides and output only during the time the signal is more negative than the low reference. Likewise, the maximum output occurs only during the time the signal is more positive than the high reference. The two signals can thus time-share the oscilloscope sweep.

The dynamic verification of a fatigue machine for constant amplitude fatigue is not a difficult matter, as long as one is careful to have adequate frequency response in all sensing and readout elements used. For random loading, especially with complex wave tests, the situation is more difficult. One can either use a "basic" method involving the detailed analysis of the signal using digital devices, or one can use a constant amplitude sinewave signal at various frequencies (in the frequency range used), and determine how accurately the signal is read. For example, the root mean square level should be 70.7 percent of the maximum amplitude of the constant amplitude signal. This indirect technique is often referred to as a "cross-calibration."

In certain cases, the verification may include consideration of the waveform shape. A distortion analysis can be made of a constant amplitude sinewave using standard electronic instruments, which determine the root mean square level of the deviations from a perfect sinewave, as a percentage of the double amplitude.

Two further points should be borne in mind by the fatigue investigator. Firstly, calibration load cells used in both tension and compression often show a significant shift (for example, 2 to 4 percent) in the load-output slope between tension and compression. This discontinuity in slope should be documented in tests involving reversed loading. Secondly, grips can have appreciable masses. Since one of the grips is in motion during a dynamic test, the inertia effects of the grip will cause a difference between the dynamic and static response of the machine.

While it is true that it is not yet possible to perform dynamic calibration, it remains to be seen whether the static calibration, with due allowance for frequency response and inertia effects, is sufficient for practical purposes in fatigue testing. A study of the dynamic response of dynamometers used for dynamic testing would clarify this point.

An Example of a Machine Calibration—The emphasis in this section has been on axial-load fatigue machines, although the principles have a general application. A brief discussion, therefore, of the method of calibration of an R.R. Moore rotating bending machine might be helpful. Figure 58 illustrates the arrangement of the loading system in such a machine.

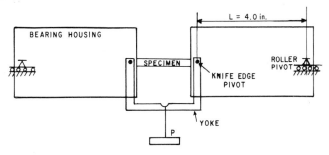

FIG. 58—*Schematic diagram of R. R. Moore testing machine.*

This arrangement results in a constant bending moment of value $PL/2$ over the length of the specimen. The nominal stress (σ_N) is given by the relation

$$\sigma_N = \frac{16PL}{\pi d^3}$$

The theoretical maximum error is given by

$$\left(\frac{\Delta \sigma_N}{\sigma_N}\right)_{max} = \frac{\Delta P}{P} + \frac{\Delta L}{L} + \frac{3\Delta d}{d}$$

In a particular case as described in Ref *31*, L was 4.0 in. (101.6 mm), d was 0.240 in. (6.1 mm), and a representative value of P was 70 lb (32 kg).

The specimen dimensions were measured using an optical comparator with a magnification of 100, Δd was found to be less than 0.0003 in. (0.0076 mm). The equivalent weight of housings, yokes, and weight hangers was determined and the weights themselves were weighed; the resulting value of ΔP was 0.09 lb (0.041 kg). The bending arms, L, were measured to 0.02 in. (0.51 mm), making $\Delta L = 0.02$. The total error is then 0.01, and the value of the stress should be within ±1 percent of the nominal. This finding was subsequently checked by means of a specimen instrumented with electrical resistance strain gages. The load cycle showed no measurable deviation from the expected sinewave, and the maximum error in the stress was only 3/4 percent.

7.4 Overall Accuracy

The best way to present an overall picture for each test system or machine is with a table such as shown in Table 1. Each of the various factors will be discussed briefly so that the table may be better appreciated.

7.4.1. Static and Dynamic Accuracy

Static accuracy is the accuracy obtained when the system is maintaining a given load, strain, or position with essentially no ram (crosshead) movement.

Dynamic accuracy is the accuracy of the load peaks or the accuracy of the peak to peak amplitude when operating a cyclic test. This accuracy varies considerably, depending upon which of these is referred to and at what speed or cyclic rate. At very slow speeds, the accuracy approaches the static accuracy; however, at higher speeds (as limited by the response of the test system), the accuracy is usually much less. Generally, the most important accuracy under high-speed conditions is the "readout" or "indicated" accuracy.

Dynamic accuracy could also, under special circumstances, refer to the ability of a system to follow a given program input (Fig. 59).

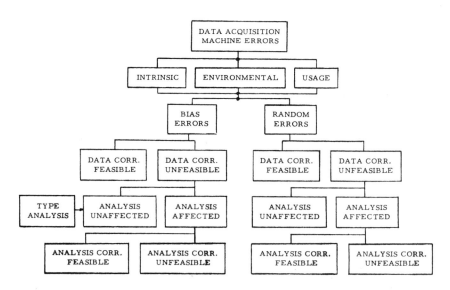

FIG. 59—*Classification of machine errors depending on type analysis.*

TABLE 1—*An example of systems accuracy specifications.*

Test Parameter	Transducer	System Accuracy			
		Static Readout Accuracy	Dynamic Readout Accuracy	Programmer Accuracy	Short-Term Control Stability
Load	Strain gage load cell	1% of reading or 0.1% of range, whichever is greater but never greater than 0.5% of range As read on digital load indicator. Add approx. 0.2% for X-Y recorder range.	1% of range on high speed strip chart recorder 0.25% of range when using amplitude measurement panel *Add correction factor for grip *g* force.	0.25% for cyclic function generator	0.05% of range
Stroke	LVDT displacement transducer. Coincidentally mounted in actuator shaft	0.75% of range as read on X-Y recorder	1.5% of range on high speed strip recorder up to 100 Hz. 2% up to 200 Hz	Same as above	0.075% of range
Strain	Strain gage extensometer	0.5% of range as read on X-Y recorder	2% of range on high speed strip chart recorder up to 50 Hz	Same as above	0.1% of range

7.4.2 Readout Accuracy

There are usually several transducers and associated conditioners for each fatigue test system which produce different accuracies for each of the transducer/conditioner combinations, Fig. 59. These are load, stroke (or crosshead position), and strain.

The readout accuracy is the accuracy of the indicated parameter (for example, load or strain) with respect to the actual load or strain as seen by the test specimen. This must be clearly identified as:

1. percent of transducer range,
2. percent of transducer conditioner range, and
3. percent of actual value.

To view this clearly, it is helpful to consider the static and dynamic readout accuracies separately.

Static Readout Accuracy—

1. Static load readout accuracy must be at least 1 percent of applied load or 0.1 percent of load range, whichever is greater. This is a minimum to meet ASTM E 4-64 specifications.
2. Static strain readout accuracy is primarily a function of the strain transducer and its associated transducer conditioner. Three types of strain transducers are typically possible: one bonded to or attached directly to a specimen, one that is a differential transformer (LVDT), and one that is an optical, noncontacting type.

Dynamic Readout Accuracy—

1. Dynamic load readout accuracy is dependent upon testing speed or cyclic rate. At low frequencies (under 0.5 Hz), conventional strip chart and X-Y recorders can be used as the indicator. At low to medium frequencies, high-speed direct writing recorders and oscillo-graphs can be used, while at high frequencies, oscillographs and oscilloscopes must be used. The accuracy of the load signal from the load transducer conditioner is the same as the static accuracies up to approximately 100 Hz. To this, we must add the accuracy of the readout instrument and also the load error due to the inertia forces on the grips between the specimen and the load cell.

    The most accurate dynamic readout is obtained using an oscillo-scope as a simple null indicator in conjunction with a precision static offset signal. Accuracies in the order of 0.25 percent of load range are obtainable using this technique.
2. Dynamic strain/stroke readout accuracy is affected by essentially the same factors as load readout accuracy except that, while the grip mass does not have an effect, the mass of the extensometer (if it is

attached to the specimen) does. Other factors are type of extenso-meter, its frequency response, and, the frequency response of the transducer conditioner. Each example must be considered separately.

7.4.3. Control Accuracy

Control accuracy is the accuracy with which the system can provide and maintain the desired programmed value. For example, if a static load of 50 000 lb is programmed on a 100 000-lb test system but the system provided 49 750 lb and maintained this load within ±250 lb, then the accuracy would be 1 percent of load or ½ percent of range. Here again, one must specify the accuracy as either (1) percent of load range or (2) percent of actual load.

Whereas readout accuracy is the same for each range, control accuracy is not as good for the magnified ranges. It is also dependent upon the characteristics of the various components in the servo system (such as relative size of servovalve to actuator or dynamic performance of the servovalve or both), transducers, and signal conditioners.

Under normal laboratory conditions, the static control accuracy and stability is within 0.25 percent of range. The dynamic control accuracy must be specified for each system and at specific speeds or operating frequencies.

7.4.4. Program Accuracy

Each of the different programmers and the various recording or indicating instruments must be considered when determining the accuracy to which each programmer can provide the desired program signal. The accuracy range is very wide, varying from as much as a few percent of full scale for a tape recorder to 0.25 percent of full scale for some cyclic function generators. An important consideration is that most program-mers are operated at their 100 percent output and the signal is simply potentiometrically attenuated at the controller input. This means that the accuracy is a direct percent of setting plus accuracy of the attenuator, rather than percent of feedback.

The dynamic and static accuracies are essentially the same for the various programmers used.

7.4.5. Overall Accuracy

Overall accuracy can be considered in terms of either the applied load or the load range as indicated earlier. It is important, therefore, to be specific when making statements relating to this accuracy.

Basically, overall accuracy is the accuracy to which the system will generate a load or strain in a test specimen in response to the set (or desired) program. Although it could be considered the same as both the program and control accuracy, the accuracy is usually somewhat better than their sum because it is unlikely that the maximum deviations of both of them would be coincident. Figures 60 to 63 illustrate the sequence of calculations to determine the overall accuracy of two transducers independently and as part of the total system.

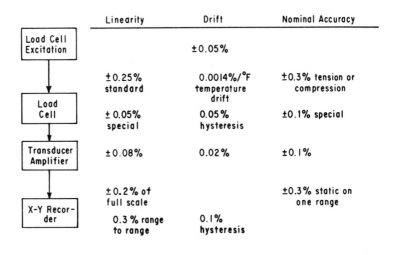

FIG. 60—*Load cell accuracy sequence.*

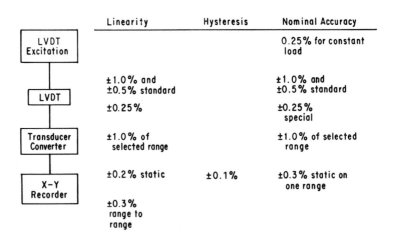

FIG. 61—*LVDT transducer accuracy sequence.*

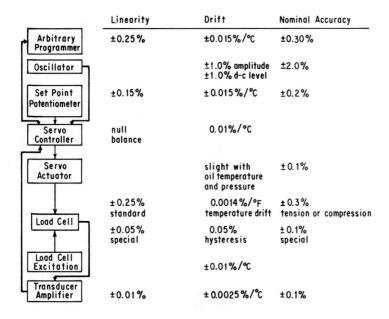

	Linearity	Drift	Nominal Accuracy
Arbitrary Programmer	±0.25%	±0.015%/°C	±0.30%
Oscillator		±1.0% amplitude ±1.0% d-c level	±2.0%
Set Point Potentiometer	±0.15%	±0.015%/°C	±0.2%
Servo Controller	null balance	0.01%/°C	
Servo Actuator		slight with oil temperature and pressure	±0.1%
Load Cell	±0.25% standard	0.0014%/°F temperature drift	±0.3% tension or compression
	±0.05% special	0.05% hysteresis	±0.1% special
Load Cell Excitation		±0.01%/°C	
Transducer Amplifier	±0.01%	±0.0025%/°C	±0.1%

FIG. 62—*Typical programmer—load cell—accuracy sequence.*

	Linearity	Drift	Nominal Accuracy
Arbitrary Programmer	±0.15%	±0.05%	±0.25%
Oscillator		±0.25% amplitude ±0.25% d-c level	±1.0%
Set Point Pot	±0.15 %	±0.05%	±0.2%
Servo Controller	null balance	0.01%/°C	
Servo Actuator		slight with oil temperature and pressure	±0.1%
to transducer conditioner	to LVDT		

FIG. 63—*Typical programmer—LVDT accuracy sequence.*

Some types of programmers, such as digital processors (computers) and other digital programmers, provide program correction in response to the readout signal. Therefore, the overall accuracy when using these devices is the same, or better, than the control accuracy.

The high values of absolute error in the lower load ranges is often handled by switching in more sensitive ranges for the same dynamometer, or by switching to more sensitive dynamometers.

The term "overall accuracy" is often interpreted in the following manner as applied to two different types of systems.

Applied to an open-loop or manually controlled hydraulic or screw-driven machine, overall accuracy means the accuracy of the actual load applied to the test specimen with respect to that read on the load indicator.

The same expression when applied to a closed-loop system usually means the accuracy of the load applied to the test specimen with respect to that set on the program command. Under these circumstances, the older style open-loop machine usually has a better accuracy. However, if the accuracies of the machines are compared on the same basis, there is normally little difference.

The most common problem in assessing overall accuracy lies in the "summing" of individual errors. It is important, at this point, to realize just what "error" means. If all errors were predictable, they could be compensated for in the manner of a "standard correction." Most errors are, unfortunately, not actually predictable; rather, the maximum error to be reasonably expected is stated. The "summing" of these random values is, therefore, a matter of summing probabilities for the individual error values.

Reference 34 shows from probability analysis that, for random errors which are roughly equal in size and symmetrically probable (plus or minus values equally possible) about a datum level, the root mean square value of the individual error values, is the most likely value for the total overall error. Thus, the root mean square of the errors defines the overall accuracy. Of course, bias or predictable (systematic) errors cannot be treated from the probability standpoint; such determinate errors are simply added directly.

References

[31] Cicci, F., "An Investigation of the Statistical Distribution of Constant Amplitude Fatigue Endurances for a Maraging Steel," UTIAS Technical Note 73, July 1964.
[32] Elevated Temperature Testing Problem Areas STP 488, American Society for Testing and Materials, 1971.
[33] Serensen, S. V., Garf, M. E., and Kuz'menko, V. A., "The Dynamics of a Fatigue Testing Machine," trans. from Russian, published for U.S. Dept. of Commerce, TT 70-50033, Israel Program for Science Translation, Jerusalem, 1970.
[34] Lockery, H. E., Measurement Topics, Vol. 1, No. 2, March 1971.
[35] Dowell, T. M., "Dynamic Calibration of Fatigue-Testing Machines," Engineering, 30 May 1958.

Chapter 8—Monitoring Fatigue Testing

The amount of technical information generated by a single fatigue test can vary from a terse noting of the cycles or time to the point when the specimen broke into two pieces, to the continuous observation of dislocation movement by means of television or movie camera. It is outside the scope of this manual to discuss the examination of the specimen after failure (for example, fractography). However, the fatigue test engineer should know something of the wide range of possibilities he can utilize to monitor what is happening on and in the specimen during the test. In this chapter, a number of techniques for monitoring cyclic strain, crack initiation, and crack propagation will be briefly described. For more detailed information, the reader is advised to consult the bibliography at the end of the chapter.

There are, roughly speaking, two stages in the development of fatigue damage.

1. The crack initiation phase. In this phase, in contrast with localized "macrodamage," general "microdamage" is taking place, leading to the development of one or more microcracks.

2. Creation and propagation of a dominant crack. In this phase, one area of "microdamage" has grown to such an extent that its geometrical effect is no longer microscopic and isolated, but is rather a coordinated phenomenon of an order of magnitude greater than the isolated activity. For example, the cleavage of a grain through a grain boundary, to set up a crack spanning more than one grain, may be regarded as the transition between the two phases.

The actual transition point here is dependent upon, among other things, how closely the specimen is being monitored and is not of great importance in the present discussion. What is significant is that the methods of monitoring fatigue damage are quite different in each of the two stages.

There are very few devices which directly monitor changes in bulk properties; for example, small changes in conductivity due to slip band formation may be monitored by ultra-sensitive eddy current probes. Progress has been made, however, in the indirect measurement of these changes through the use of identically loaded fatigue-sensitive elements called fatigue life gages, which are cemented (or otherwise attached) to the part so that they are strain-loaded by the strains in the parent material.

By choosing gage material which yields appreciable changes in its bulk properties (in this case, electrical resistivity), the "damage" developing in the parent material can be estimated.

For many nonmetallic materials, "bulk" fatigue damage can be monitored by gross changes in the deformation taking place. It is not necessary with such materials for a crack to be present in order for them to deflect significantly as they suffer fatigue damage (for example, composites, wood, etc.).

8.1 Measurement of Cyclic Strain

Cyclic strains, and the changes which occur during the course of a fatigue test, may be monitored satisfactorily by means of high-quality extensometry, particularly in the low-cycle (high strain) range. Contacting or noncontacting extensometers may be used and ASTM *Manual on Low Cycle Fatigue Testing* (ASTM STP 465) describes the techniques of load and strain monitoring in such tests.

8.1.1. Contacting Extensometers

Several types of contacting extensometers are commerically available, utilizing either strain gages or linear variable differential transformers (LVDT's) as the sensing devices. Figures 64 and 65 show two different types of contacting extensometers. The former monitors axial strain by using bonded strain gages to measure bending in the cantilever arms. The latter monitors diametral strain by means of an LVDT.

Contacting extensometers must meet a number of requirements for use under dynamic conditions typical of fatigue loading. These requirements include the following.

1. Negligible short-term drift. This is defined as the change in reading from the initial instant of strain application, until the signal has a steady value. Typically, there will be a small but measurable change in reading up to 10 to 20 s after strain application. While this results in a difference between "dynamic" and "static" reading, it is usually negligible.
2. Negligible long-term drift. This refers to the ability of the extensometer to hold its calibration over long periods (hours, days) and can be easily determined by preliminary calibrations over about 24 h of continuous cycling.
3. Satisfactory static calibration. In this phase of the verification of the extensometer, the readings are calibrated against a standard (calibration devices, gage-blocks) in a stepwise manner. For further details, the reader is referred to ASTM Standard Method of Verification and Classification of Extensometers (E 83-67). The following

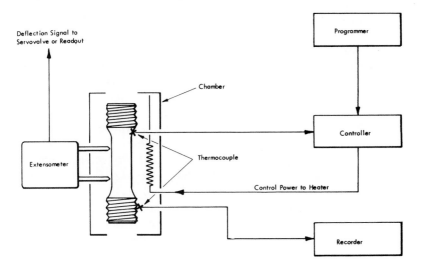

FIG. 64—*System functional diagram of a typical strain gage extensometer.*

FIG. 65—*Sketch of a simple diametral strain extensometer. Strain gages in the curved sections measure cantilever deflection.*

table is a general guide to the terminology used in specifying extensometer accuracy.

Class of Extensometer	Maximum Error of Indicated Strain
A	10×10^{-6}
B1	100×10^{-6}
B2	200×10^{-6}
C	1000×10^{-6}

4. Negligible hysteresis error. ASTM E 83-67 applies usually only to monotonically increasing or decreasing strain. For fatigue purposes it is necessary to consider the case of alternating strain. The degree of error on changing the direction of the strain values must be assessed.

5. Satisfactory frequency response. The use of contacting extensometers in fatigue is generally restricted to slow cycling, since higher frequencies will damage the instruments. There is, of course, a boundary in the amplitude-frequency plane applicable to a given extensometer. This boundary should be indicated adequately. For example, it is insufficient to specify that an extensometer has frequency response capability to about 200 Hz, if the amplitude associated with these frequencies is so small as to be less than the value of the error from the static calibration.

6. Negligible harmonic distortion. Harmonic distortion is a measure (in rms) of the difference between the extensometer signal under, for example, sinusoidal excitation, and a pure sinewave of the same frequency and amplitude. One can usually estimate visually from an oscilloscope, 3 percent harmonic distortion or greater (the percent is based on the ratio of root mean square deviation to maximum amplitude). Five percent distortion is often considered a limit in satisfactory extensometer performance in fatigue testing.

8.1.2. Noncontacting Extensometers

In many fatigue test situations it is difficult to attach an extensometer to the specimen; for instance, when induction coils are used around the specimen in elevated temperature fatigue studies. For such situations, noncontacting extensometers are necessary and several types of optical extensometers are possible, using either normal light or laser light. A functional schematic diagram for an axial extensometer of the former type is shown in Fig. 66 and a similar diagram for the latter type in Fig. 67. Such devices are used with separate heads (for each gage pin) or with a single head using a split-field viewer, Fig. 68. The latter arrangement combines the sensitivity needed for actual strains with the range needed to observe both gage pins (separated by gage lengths of 1/2 in. (12.7 mm) or more).

8.2 Measurements of Fatigue Damage—Crack Initiation and Propagation

A wide variety of experimental methods have been used to study the changes taking place in a specimen while it is being subjected to alternating stress. Since the development of a definite crack causes the most marked change in properties, most of these methods are used primarily to detect a crack at the earliest possible stage or to measure the

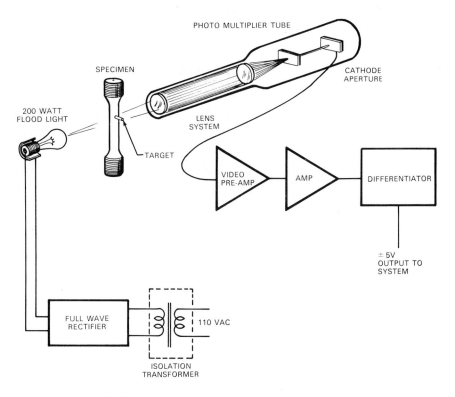

FIG. 66—*Functional schematic of the optical extensometer.*

growth of the crack. However, many of them are capable of responding to more subtle variations in properties which may be of importance in particular studies.

Once a dominant crack exists, it can be monitored in a number of different ways. Considering the simplest first, one can monitor the stiffness of the specimen during fatigue testing by electronically dividing the load signal by the strain signal. Reduction in stiffness is, however, a rather crude approach, since in many specimens a crack has to be very large indeed for a change in the (gross) stiffness to occur.

Visual—Manual Techniques

Flat sheet specimens are normally chosen for measurement of crack propagation rates and interpretation or analysis in terms of phenomenological or fracture mechanics theories. Tests are usually made in tension-compression or tension-tension loading. Conventional fatigue machines are quite suitable for this type of investigation and it is only occasionally that

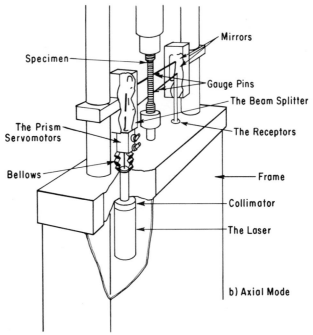

FIG. 67—*A noncontacting extensometer for fatigue testing, using a laser beam. The obstruction of the beam is monitored on the reception.*

the demands of a particular investigation warrant the construction of a special test apparatus.

For visual observation of the specimen during tests, it is usually necessary to have a stroboscopic light source and a means for triggering the light at any desired point in the stress cycle. Good sensitivity for crack detection can be obtained in this way if the surface of the specimen is observed at moderate magnification and the light is triggered at the time of maximum tensile stress. The method is, however, very tedious and unless the test area is quite small, it is difficult to substitute time-lapse photography for visual observation. Once a crack has been observed, the area of interest is limited to that through which the crack is propagating and motion pictures can be taken readily.

Synchronized strobe lighting can be used to illuminate the specimen and moving picture records can be obtained through a special microscope focused on the tip of the growing crack.

Travelling microscopes usually are used in manual monitoring of crack length. These devices typically have 0.0004 in. (0.01 mm) repeatability and have been used with specimens heated to 540°C (1000°F).

A movie camera can also be replaced by a 35-mm still camera for time-lapse photography.

FIG. 68—*A split laser beam monitoring the relative displacement of two gage pins on a fatigue specimen heated to 1500° F.*

Examination of fracture surfaces at optical and electron-optical levels, termed fractography, has proved to be a powerful tool for study of crack extension mechanisms. Normally, special testing equipment is not required for this type of investigation, but care must be exercised so that the fracture surfaces are not subjected to scrubbing, banging, or other destructive conditions prior to examination. To avoid such damage, cyclic loading may be discontinued prior to separation and the sample pulled apart under static load for subsequent fracture surface examination, or the test may be carried out under fluctuating tension.

To establish rates of crack growth, increments of 0.01 in. (0.25 mm) can be used. This is desirable in specimens with typically 0.1 in. (2.5 mm) of thickness, so that any minor irregularities in growth between portions of the crack front throughout the thickness of the sample are averaged out in observations of growth on the surface of the sample. Moreover, using 0.01-in. (0.25-mm) increments makes it possible to use very simple instrumentation to measure crack growth.

One technique employed is the use of photographically prepared lines on the surface of the specimen perpendicular to the cracking direction and spaced at 0.02 in. (0.50 mm). This technique involves applying a photographic emulsion to the specimen surface, exposing the emulsion through a negative with carefully prepared lines, and washing off the unexposed emulsion leaving only the lines on the specimen. Viewing these lines with a 15 power ordinary magnifying glass allows the operator to observe the crack length to each one-half line location with more than sufficient accuracy. With this relatively low-power magnification and using a stiff system and specimen, it is not necessary to interrupt tests to make observations of crack length. Adjustments in lighting and polishing the specimen surfaces are necessary refinements for best results. Moreover, viewing cracks against lines on the surface of the specimen proves sufficiently easy through water and clear oil, as well as air, without having to account for optical distortion, since the crack is referenced against the lines. This technique is simple and inexpensive.

As cracks are observed progressing each 0.01 in. (0.25 mm), as shown in Fig. 69, the number of cycles required for each is recorded and a rate of growth, da/dN, is computed directly as the ratio of that distance over the number of cycles. Since for each increment the crack length and loads are known, the range of crack tip stress intensity, ΔK, may also be computed and plotted versus the growth rate, da/dN, to illustrate the material's fatigue crack growth characteristics.

Fracture Wires and Wire Grids

One convenient method of crack detection, and one that works fairly well in component testing, is the use of "fracture" wires which are available from strain gage manufacturers. These are small-diameter insulated wires that are cemented on the critical area of the specimen. When a crack propagates under the wire, the wire is also broken; the interruption to current in the wire can be used to trigger an alarm or turn off the testing machine. There are also versions which are based on the resistance change at fracture. The location of the wires is important, because if they are subjected to a high stress amplitude they will generally break before a crack has developed, thus giving a false alarm. However, in notched specimens or components it is often possible to place the wires in such a way that they are near enough to the point of stress concentration, so that

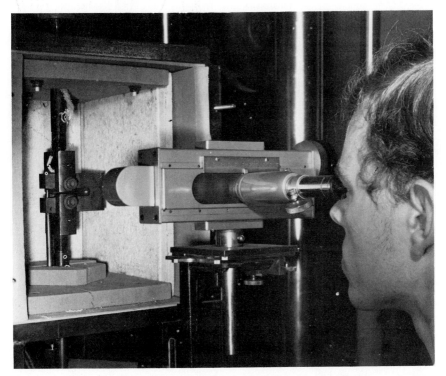

FIG. 69—*High temperature fatigue testing using a vernier telescope.*

they will be broken by a fairly small crack, without having them so close that they are subjected to a high stress amplitude. Also, premature breaks in the wires can be reduced by running a part of the expected life before the wires are applied, thus reducing the number of cycles which they must withstand. The type of cement used can also affect the fatigue behavior of the wires. The fracture wire method is generally not applicable to small, unnotched specimens.

So-called crack propagation gages are also available from strain gage manufacturers. These gages are in the form of wire grids and consist essentially of a series of 20 or more parallel, equally-spaced wires. Crack growth can be studied by monitoring the wires individually or by measuring the overall change in resistance.

Ultrasonic Method

An ultrasonic nondestructive test procedure has been developed to measure and record the extent of crack growth encountered in fatigue and

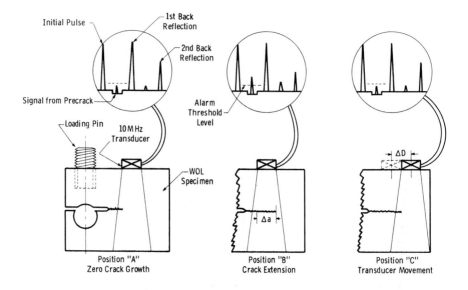

FIG. 70—*Schematic representation of the ultrasonic technique used to measure subcritical crack growth.*

stress corrosion tests involving specimens used in subcritical fatigue crack growth studies (Fig. 70). The essence of the technique is to relate the position of an ultrasonic transducer on the specimen surface to the tip of the propagating crack such that crack length can be interpreted in terms of transducer location. The required instrumentation includes commercially available ultrasonic flaw detection equipment and a test fixture (Fig. 71) designed to permit completely automatic measurement of crack growth. The technique yields a crack length measurement sensitivity of ±0.010 in. (0.25 mm) and provides a continuous record of crack length versus elapsed time which, in turn, can readily be converted into crack growth rate data.

Electrical Potential Method

Figure 72 illustrates schematically an electrical potential device used to monitor crack growth. Figure 73 is a representation of the way in which the electrical potential will be changed in the presence of a crack.

This technique has been used successfully by several workers. It requires care in the setting of the sensors on the specimen and can be insensitive in cases where the total crack length is relatively small.

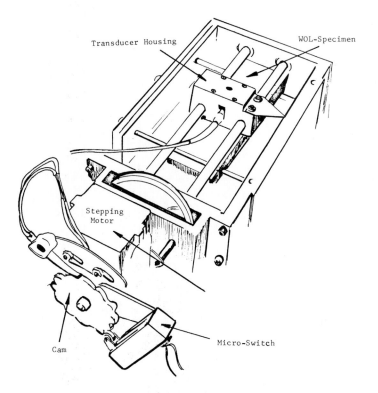

FIG. 71—*Test fixture used to monitor crack growth.*

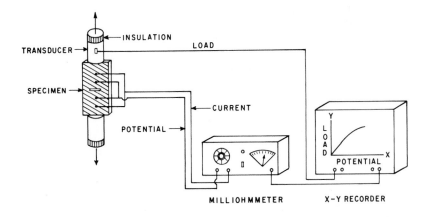

FIG. 72—*Schematic drawing of electric-potential measurement and recording setup.*

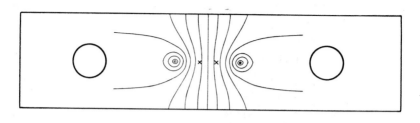

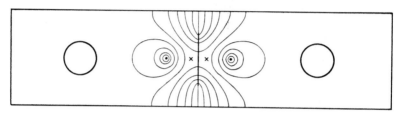

FIG. 73—*Electric-potential field distributions* (*equipotential lines*) (top) *without a crack and* (bottom) *with a crack.*

Eddy Currents

It is often difficult to have sufficient contact discrimination to keep visual track of the tip of a fatigue crack on a surface of uniform reflectivity. This problem is catered to very well by eddy-current devices, which see the crack as a large perturbation contrasting strongly with the background of uncracked sheet. Also, they have reasonable power to penetrate the top surface layers to some degree, to obtain an accurate and stable signal.

The eddy-current method is essentially a combination of a magnetic method and a local resistance measuring technique. Automation is simple and there are no special coupling problems. Crack monitoring is continuous, and the servo-system is arranged for automatic crack-following.

Since the eddy-current device supplies an electrical signal of the presence of a crack, a probe at the end of a servo-controlled linear actuator can be positioned at the side of a specimen notch. By enclosing the probe in a nylon sheath, it is possible to keep the probe surface a fixed distance (0.010 in.) (0.25 mm) from the sheet surface, preventing any damage to the probe when the specimen fractures into two pieces.

As soon as the crack appears, the eddy-current off-null signal is used to drive the linear actuator horizontally to the right (Fig. 74). The probe is then moved physically to the right. When the probe reaches the crack tip,

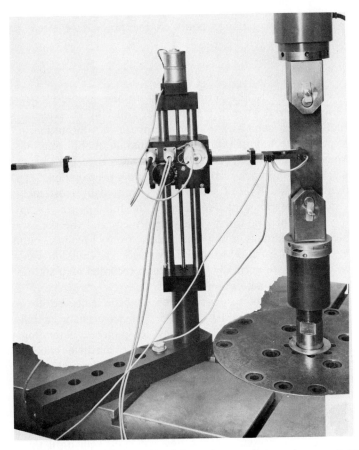

FIG. 74—*The monitoring of crack length in a sheet specimen, using a servo-controlled eddy current crack follower.*

the off-null signal drops to zero, which stops the servo actuator. In this way the actuator system, having high response, is "locked on" to the tip of the crack. The crack signal could also be used to actuate the elevator for the probe to "lock on" in the vertical dimension.

A potentiometer is coupled physically to the actuator and presents a continuous signal of actuator position. Two probe systems can be used, one on each side of the notch, and for single-notch specimens a small LVDT can be added at the edge to measure (and cancel) the transverse motion of the specimen.

The size of the probe is not really an indication of the sensitivity of the system, since by balancing for a signal associated with, say, 70 percent penetration of the probe into uncracked material one can detect increments in crack growth of less than 0.010 in. (0.25 mm) by the resulting shift in the balance point on the probe face along the sheet surface.

Acoustic Emission

Acoustic emission is the term applied to the low level stress waves emitted by a material when it is deformed, either by an external stress or an internal process, such as a martensitic phase transformation.

Although the technique of acoustic emission monitoring has, up to recent times, been largely restricted to crack detection in metals, it provides a useful approach to the study of crack propagation.

The frequency and level of sound waves emitted by most metals under stress is not in the range of detection of the human ear, except for the emission from tin or zinc when grossly deformed, and the pop-in emission from fracture specimens when the crack front becomes momentarily unstable, and then quickly arrests. Thus, acoustic emission signals from modern structures are normally detected and recorded with state-of-the-art transducers and instrumentation.

The individual events responsible for acoustic emission from metals have rise times in the range 10^{-4} to 10^{-8} s, so an acoustic emission pulse contains a very wide range of frequency components, extending up into the megacycle range. Hence, any transducer sensitive enough to the pressure levels present will be responsive, regardless of its frequency response.

Acoustic emission from metals is related to permanent deformation processes, such as plastic deformation. The onset of plastic deformation is controlled by the presence of stress raisers, such as notches and cracks. If no stress raisers are present, plastic flow will not begin until the nominal stresses are close to the general yield level. However, if stress raisers are present, plastic deformation will begin at nominal stress levels considerably below general yield, which will result in acoustic emission at low stresses. Hence, the presence of stress raisers greatly effects the nominal stress level at which acoustic emission begins, and monitoring for acoustic emission provides a technique for the detection in structures of the presence of stress raisers, such as cracks and other types of flaws.

It is possible to detect fatigue crack growth by continuous acoustic emission monitoring. However, the presence of background noise during service and the high expense would make continuous monitoring of acoustic emission impractical in most situations of technological interest. As an alternative to continuous monitoring, a procedure which takes advantage of the irreversibility of acoustic emission is possible.

If a cracked specimen of structure is loaded to a particular value of the stress intensity factor (K), and then unloaded, emission will not occur during reloading until the previous value of K is exceeded. It is possible to take advantage of this irreversible aspect to determine whether or not a crack has grown during cyclic loading at a stress σ_w, by periodically over-stressing (proof-testing) the structure at a stress σ_p ($>\sigma_w$), while monitoring for acoustic emission. If flaws have grown at σ_w since the previous overstress, then the stress intensity factor during proof testing ($K \propto \tau_p a^{1/2}$) will have increased, and emission will be observed during the proof test. Alternatively, if no crack growth occurred at σ_w, K_p would remain the same as during the previous proof test and no new plastic deformation (and hence no acoustic emission) would occur.

Although acoustic emission is an indirect measure of actual crack length, it is an "active" sensor (the crack makes itself known) in contrast to the "passive" devices described earlier.

Bibliography

Adams, N. J. I. and Munro, H. G., *Strain*, Vol. 5, April 1969, pp. 68-73.

Anctil, A. A., Kula, E. B., and DiCesare, E., "Electrical-Potential Technique for Determining Slow Crack Growth," Advance Paper presented at the 66th Annual Meeting of the American Society for Testing and Materials, 23-28 June 1965.

Brook, R. H. W. and Parry, J. S. C., *Journal of Mechanical Engineering Science*, Vol. 11, No. 3, 1969, pp. 243-255.

Christensen, R. H. in *Metal Fatigue*, McGraw-Hill Book Co., 1959, pp. 376-412.

Dunegan, H. L. and Tetelman, A. S., "Non-Destructive Characterization of Hydrogen-Embrittlement Cracking by Acoustic Emission Techniques," Technical Bulletin DRC-106, Dunegan Research Corp., Livermore, Calif.

Harris, D. O., Dunegan, H. L., and Tetelman, A. S., "Prediction of Fatigue Lifetime by Combined Fracture Mechanics and Acoustic Emission Techniques," UCRL-71760, Technical Bulletin DRC-105, Dunegan Research Corp., Livermore, Calif.

Harting, D. R., *Experimental Mechanics*, Vol. 6, Feb. 1966, pp. 19A-24A.

James, Lee A., "The Effect of Elevated Temperature Upon the Fatigue-Crack Propagation Behaviour of Two Austenitic Stainless Steels," International Conference on Mechanical Behavior of Materials, 15-20 Aug. 1971, Kyoto, Japan, WHAN-SA-105.

Johnson, H. H., *Materials Research and Standards*, Vol. 5, Sept. 1965, p. 442.

Li, Che-Yu and Wei, R. P., *Materials Research and Standards*, Aug. 1966, pp. 392-394.

Linge, J. R., *Aircraft Engineering*, Vol. 29, Nov. 1957, pp. 334-342.

Packman, P. F., Pearson, H. S., Owens, J. S., and Young, G., *Journal of Materials*, Vol. 4, Sept. 1969, pp. 666-700.

Scott, I. G., "The Early Detection of Fatigue Cracking," ARL Metallurgy Note 62, Australian Dept. of Supply, Feb. 1962.

Slot, T. and Stentz, R. H., "Experimental Methods for Low-Cycle Fatigue Research at High Temperatures," SESA Meeting Paper, Ottawa, GEMP 527, May 1967.

Thomas, E. D. R., *Experimental Mechanics*, Vol. 10, Aug. 1970, pp. 346-352.

Chapter 9—Environments for Fatigue Testing

Studies of crack growth behavior have shown that fatigue resistance (crack growth rate, crack initiation time) can be very sensitive to the environment. For example, while the shape of the waveform is generally unimportant in constant amplitude fatigue testing in normal air-conditioned rooms, there are many situations with moderately "hostile" environments, where a small change of waveform profile (changing the time to and at the higher stress levels in each cycle) will cause a significant change in crack growth rate.

The use of any artificially-controlled environment complicates a test by increasing the complexity of associated equipment required and makes the procedures more involved for installing and removing a specimen, observing failure, and monitoring progress of the test. Precautionary measures to prevent endangering the health and safety of operators and others in the vicinity of equipment are also important where volatile, toxic or explosive materials are involved.

This chapter is not meant to be a comprehensive coverage of this topic. It is presented rather as a descriptive overview to underline the importance of the environment in fatigue testing. Several recent ASTM publications have covered a number of topics in this area.

9.1 Corrosive Environments

The fatigue strength of materials is often more sensitive to the chemical environment than are other mechanical properties, so that environmental control is an important factor in fatigue testing. The combination of a mild corrosive agent and alternating stress is much more damaging than either one alone; even the constituents of the normal indoor atmosphere are slightly corrosive to most structural metals, so that fatigue strength determined in the conventional test is usually lower than that found when the atmosphere is excluded. These effects are accentuated by elevated temperature, often necessitating the use of inert gas atmospheres. With some materials such as the aluminum alloys, the fatigue behavior is influenced to a market extent by the amount of water vapor in the air. For this reason, it is well to control the humidity of the fatigue test environment within reasonably close limits in order to minimize scatter of the results due to this factor.

The simultaneous action of a corrosive environment and fluctuating stress is referred to as corrosion fatigue. The frequency of the testing machine, which is of minor importance in conventional tests, has a marked effect on the fatigue life under corrosion fatigue conditions. Also, it must be remembered that corrosion may be taking place even when the specimen is not being stressed, and the damage resulting from this action can lower the fatigue strength of the metal significantly. Corrosion is a time-dependent phenomenon, while fatigue in itself is usually only cycle-dependent (Figs. 75 and 76).

Corrosive environments are usually in the form of liquids, vapors, or gases which surround the member being fatigued (Fig. 75). The method of producing corrosion in a fatigue test varies. A stream of water has been used as the corrosive agent in some tests; salt sprays have also been applied.

To determine the effect of oleophobic films on metal fatigue, one can slip a short length of tightly fitting polyethylene tubing over the cylindrical shanks of a conventional rotating beam fatigue specimen, and fill the tube with liquid. It should be noted that in this method, the volume between the specimen and the tube is quite small so that the nature of the environment may be changed by reaction with the specimen to a much greater degree than would be the case if the specimen were surrounded by a large quantity of liquid.

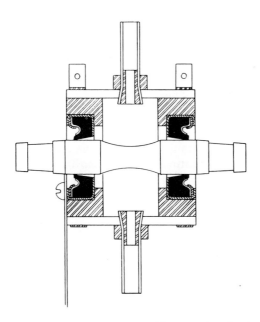

FIG. 75—*Rotating beam test with a corrosion chamber.*

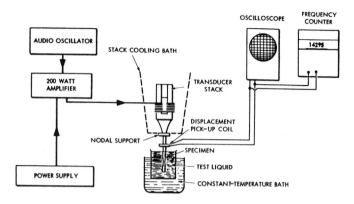

FIG. 76—*Block diagram of a magnetostriction apparatus used for high frequency fatigue tests.*

If it is desired to investigate the effect of humidity on fatigue, for example, air from a laboratory supply or a small pump is either passed through a drying tower or bubbled through two water bottles. It is then led to an environmental test chamber. The exhaust from the chamber is passed over a sensing element for an electrical humidity indicator, then exhausted under 5 to 10 mm of water in order to keep the chamber above atmospheric pressure.

Because of the very severe interactions, the most useful information on corrosion fatigue is obtained by testing laboratory specimens under conditions which most nearly simulate service. Many laboratory tests have been run to determine the "order of merit" of various materials subjected to a specific type of corrosive environment, such as seawater.

Artificial Seawater

Artificial seawater is a simulated sea salt mix containing elements found in natural sea salt in quantities greater than 0.004 percent. The salt is granular and colorless; the particles are no larger than those that will pass a 24 mesh screen. The composition of artificial seawater is based on 77 composite analyses of seawater with average total solids content of 35 600 ppm. These salts can be made according to Formula A, ASTM Specification for Substitute Ocean Water (D 1141-52).

Natural seawaters are often the best choice for simulation, if facilities are convenient.

9.2 Elevated Temperature Testing

There are several different ways to achieve high temperature; radiant

FIG. 77—*Axial load fatigue test arrangement using a salt water environment.*

(Fig. 64), resistive (Fig. 79), and inductive heating (Figs. 68 and 78) are the methods normally considered. The factors involved in the choice are:

1. the specimen material,
2. the side or awkwardness of the specimen,
3. the range of temperature desired,
4. the degree of control required,
5. the thermal gradient (with time),
6. the anticipated service heating mechanism, and
7. cost.

Protection of the specimen from oxidation or other effects is often required. This is accomplished sometimes by using a vacuum, and

FIG. 78—*An environmental test system simulating high temperature conditions.*

sometimes by the flow of inert gases. The best heating method for a particular application will depend upon the relative importance of these factors.

In many cases with elevated temperature tests, one must be prepared for specimen creep, especially if non-zero mean stresses are used in the fatigue cycle. This anticipation applies not only to freedom to elongate under load, but also to monitor accurately such elongation with readout devices. Figure 80 shows a special high temperature extensometer used for fatigue involving slow cycling.

The temperature level substantially influences the strength of materials and, to a lesser extent, the stiffness of a material. Therefore, if a test is intended to evaluate fatigue behavior at some predetermined temperature, any change in temperature during the test is undesirable. However, even for stresses low enough to be treated as elastic, there is some energy or heat generated in the specimen during cycling. The amount of energy generated in the specimen is controlled by the hysteresis characteristics of the material itself, the stress level and the volume of material at the peak stress. At the same time as it is being generated within the specimen, this heat is also being dissipated into the atmosphere or into other parts of the machine from which it is transferred into the atmosphere. Whether heat can be dissipated fast enough to prevent excessive temperature rise in the

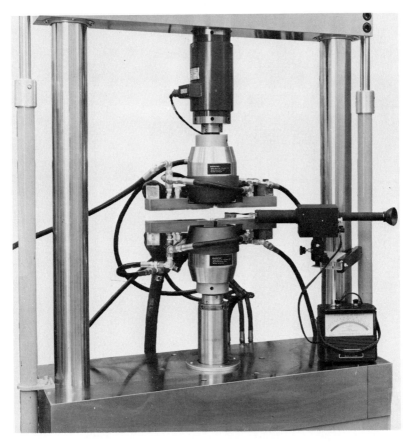

FIG. 79—*An example of a fatigue test system utilizing resistance heating for the fatigue specimen.*

specimen depends on the rate of generation and on the thermal conductivity and heat transfer conditions of the interfaces between the specimen, the machine, and the atmosphere.

Thermal Stresses

Although fatigue investigations usually have been concerned with the response of materials to cyclic or fluctuating forces, many modern applications involve cyclic thermal stressing produced by repeated stresses of thermal origin. The treatment of this problem is different from the classical problem for three reasons.

1. The severity of thermal effects may produce failure in a relatively few

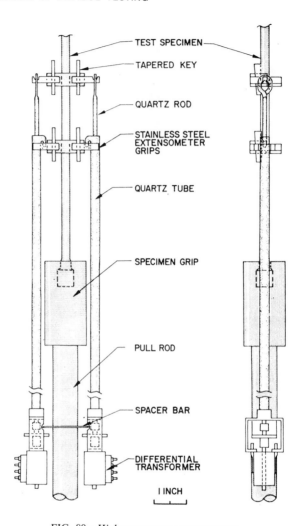

TEST SPECIMEN

TAPERED KEY

QUARTZ ROD

STAINLESS STEEL
EXTENSOMETER
GRIPS

QUARTZ TUBE

SPECIMEN GRIP

PULL ROD

SPACER BAR

DIFFERENTIAL
TRANSFORMER

I INCH

FIG. 80—*High temperature extensometer.*

cycles. That is, the low-cycle fatigue region usually predominates in thermal stressing.

2. Stresses result from fluctuating strain rather than fluctuating stress since the phenomena are related to thermal expansion. This results in large nonlinear plastic stress-strain behavior.

3. The application of thermal stress may be of low frequency with extended periods of steady-state operation. This may result in thermally activated processes such as relaxation, aging, and oxidation.

Considering a rigidly-held specimen cycled between temperatures T_1 and

T_2, and the point of rigid attachment of the bar to the frame to correspond to T_2, the resulting thermal strains can be calculated. Because the frame is rigid, the thermal strain ε_t, accompanying the lowering of the temperature to T_1 is directly equal to the mechanical strain in the specimen ε_m. Thus

$$\varepsilon_m + \varepsilon_t = 0$$

When the lower temperature T_1 is reached, the mechanical strain resulting is referred to as the strain range ε_m such that

$$\Delta\varepsilon_m = \Delta\varepsilon_t = a(T_2 - T_1)$$

where a is the longitudinal thermal expansion coefficient. The mechanical strain may be a combination of elastic and plastic strains, ε_e and ε_p. In the first few cycles of temperature, the cyclic stress-strain behavior leads to the development of a gradually stabilizing hysteresis loop. The detailed features of the stress-strain curves depend on many factors, including the material, the temperature limits, the rate of change of temperature, the dwell or "hold time," and the number of cycles.

Stress relaxation can also occur during "dwell" at elevated temperature, if the cycling is between strain limits. The hysteresis loop is characterized in terms of its elastic and plastic components such that

$$\Delta\varepsilon_m = \Delta\varepsilon_e + \Delta\varepsilon_p$$

and by its height, ΔS, called the stress range. Because the elastic strain range can be calculated as $\Delta S/E$

$$\Delta\varepsilon_p = \Delta\varepsilon_m - \Delta S/E$$

The plastic strain range $\Delta\varepsilon_p$ is a very important quantity in assessing the effect of thermal stress fatigue.

Aside from the effects of frequency and temperature, there are other variables which influence the response of metals to fluctuating thermal stress. The addition of steady stresses has important consequences. First, there is the possibility of cyclic growth, wherein the combined action of cyclic plastic strain and steady stress can lead to a progressive shift in the hysteresis (Fig. 29). Another important variable is that of sequential loading.

Finally, it should be pointed out that, except where a high degree of anisotropy in thermal expansion coefficients exists or where creep effects become important, there is little difference between thermal cycling and strain cycling at constant temperature, provided a correct choice of constant temperature is made when making a comparison. Under these conditions, thermal stressing can be viewed primarily as a means of producing cyclic plastic strain in structures which does not introduce any unique behavior of the material.

All that is needed to perform thermal stress tests is a programmable heating system and the necessary mechanical constraint of the specimen. Various methods of heating and cooling have been used. Resistance heating of the specimen by an applied electrical current, and followed by convective (fluid) cooling, is very often used. Tubular specimens are the most convenient to use. Thermocouples are generally employed as thermal transducers.

9.3 Low-Temperature Testing

Modest Low-Temperature Testing

Many fatigue tests carried out to meet, for example, military specifications, involve the simulation of outdoor temperatures to their extreme limits, that is, —100°F or lower.

Dry ice is widely used due to its convenience and economy. However, such an agent is capable of only about —40°F). Partial (regulated) use of this coolant in conjunction with warmer agents (that is, air flow) permits the use of any temperature between room temperature and the limit for such tests.

Cryogenic Temperatures

The resistance to cyclic stressing is very important in the design of cryogenic pressure vessels, tanks, and space containers. This is because while the fatigue strength will often increase when the temperature is lowered to cryogenic levels (for example, —320°F), the notch sensitivity of the material can also increase, so that a smaller flaw is sufficient to cause catastrophic failure. Growing such flaws to critical size requires correct environmental simulation if safe estimates of fatigue life are to be obtained.

Space and missile programs require operation of components at cryogenic temperatures with or without contact with fluids. In some cases, the test systems are in the environment. In others, the test system acts through extension rods fitted with bellows, etc. There are a number of "operator safety" items to consider in the use of cryogenic test systems— vapors can accumulate, and for some coolants these can be either toxic or explosive.

9.4 Pressure or Vacumm Fatigue Testing

Space Simulation

In this case a very "hard" vacuum is required, together with the radiation environment expected in space. It is almost impossible to recreate space environments of this type on earth.

Simple Vacuum

The degree of vacuum required by service, or dictated by the program requirements, will affect the choice of apparatus used to attain the vacuum. Naturally, the harder the vacuum the more problems one encounters and the more limited will be the size of the vacuum chamber. Surface outgassing and contamination from the pumping apparatus are but two of these problems.

Resonant electromagnetic drives are quite popular for vacuum fatigue tests. Specimen extensometry is often a problem, and lately, good use has been made of noncontacting (optical) extensometers for this purpose.

Elevated Temperature Vacuum

In many cases the concurrent use of heat and vacuum permits the cancelling out of problems associated with the use of either heat or vacuum alone. Specimen design can also minimize problems (for example, tubular specimens). In these cases, the use of connecting rods and bellows is often resorted to, for transmitting the test system excitation. Figure 81 illustrates a vacuum fatigue test for wire. Figure 82 shows a schematic diagram of a system for fundamental studies of fatigue where the loading occurs through bellows.

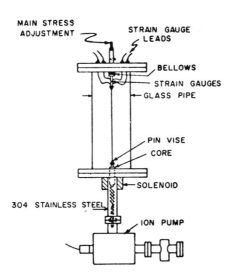

FIG. 81—Vacuum fatigue system.

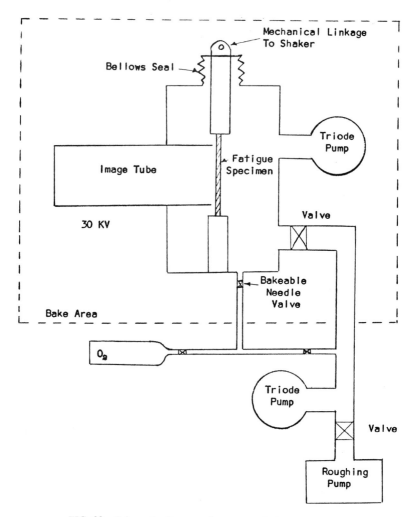

FIG. 82—*Schematic diagram of a vacuum fatigue apparatus.*

9.5 Fatigue Due to an Acoustic Environment

In aeronautical structures especially, the ability to withstand a hostile acoustic environment is quite important. Simulating such an environment is, of course, a function of a special type of fatigue test system. Several types of programmers have been used in this area.

(*a*) Discrete frequency—sirens.

(*b*) Adjustable frequency band random noise—jets.

(*c*) Sweep functions of (*a*) and (*b*).

(*d*) Modulated functions of (*a*) and (*b*).

The angle of incidence of the acoustic sound-wave is also of importance. The degree of coupling between exciter and specimen is also quite critical. The degree of reverberation of the sound can be quite different in a laboratory and in service outside.

The numerous cases of structural damage in jet aircraft, attributed to the energy associated with high intensity noise fields, are evidence of the seriousness of acoustic fatigue. The problem of design for acoustic fatigue appears to be that of reducing the amplitudes of vibration. To do this, requires a great deal of information that is not usually available. For this reason, the design approach remains largely *ad hoc* and is subjected to trial and error tests for verification of the designs selected.

Research and development work in the study of acoustic fatigue has been in five main categories.

1. Noise, the exciting force.
2. Structural response.
3. Damping and its application.
4. Structural design techniques.
5. Acoustical testing techniques and equipment.

9.6 Fretting Fatigue Testing

Fretting is the phenomenon that occurs when the surfaces of two solids are pressed together by a normal force and are caused to undergo small cyclic relative sliding motion. Usually, the normal force is large enough and the cyclic sliding motion small enough to significantly restrict the flow of debris away from its place of origin at the interface. Fretting usually gives rise to one or more forms of damage including (1) fretting corrosion, (2) fretting wear, or (3) fretting fatigue or both.

Fretting corrosion and fretting wear are any corrosion damage and wear damage, respectively, that occur as a direct result of fretting. Surface discoloration, pitting, oxide layer build-up, loss of fit, and seizing are all characteristics of these two forms of damage. Fretting fatigue is any fatigue damage attributable to fretting. The most notable characteristic of this form of damage is a reduction of fatigue strength of one or both of the parts. This reduction is frequently quite drastic in magnitude.

One researcher has listed more than 50 parameters as possibly playing an important role in fretting and fretting-induced damage. Numerous investigations have been performed to study the effect(s) of some of these parameters.

9.6.1 Fretting Fatigue Machines

A commerical rotating cantilever beam fatigue testing machine was modified at the Ohio State University to permit an investigation of the effects of fretting damage on fatigue life, Fig. 83. A fretting collet with

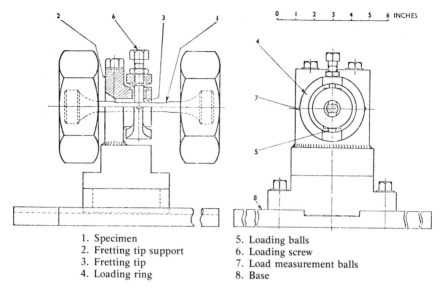

0   1   2   3   4   5   6 INCHES

1. Specimen
2. Fretting tip support
3. Fretting tip
4. Loading ring

5. Loading balls
6. Loading screw
7. Load measurement balls
8. Base

FIG. 83—*Apparatus for direct-stress fretting-fatigue experiments.*

replaceable fretting shoes was devised and mounted in the machine to apply a controlled fretting treatment at the reduced section of a conventional rotating beam fatigue test specimen, in the same manner that fretting is induced in an interference fit involving a shaft and a hub. This equipment subjected the specimen to normal pressure at the specimen shoe contact area, cyclic sliding motion between shoe and specimen due to specimen straining, and cyclic bending stress due to the load on the cantilever beam. Both the normal contact pressure and the cyclic sliding motion are a function of the cantilever load. A normal pressure also can be controlled independently by changing the specimen and shoe geometry.

A similar device was developed by Collins and Marco for producing fretting in flat plate specimens using an axial loading (direct stress) fatigue machine. The specimen is placed in series with a calibrated strain gage load cell capable of measuring static or cyclic forces in the specimen at all times. The fretting shoes are pressed against the flat surface of the specimen by a calibrated shoe loading device which provides a continuous indication of the force with which the shoes are pressed against the specimen. A static-stress preloading frame, together with a double acting load screw, is used to impose either static tensile stress, zero stress, or static compressive stress on the specimen, to move cyclically in the vertical direction, fretting is induced on both sides of the specimen. The direction of the fretting motion is parallel to the longitudinal axis of the specimen.

To produce fretting under conditions of cyclic stress, it is only necessary to remove the preloading frame from the fretting-fatigue attachment, and rigidly attach the upper end of the specimen to the frame of the testing machine.

9.7 Conclusion

At present, materials and structures must meet new environmental operating requirements which are becoming more and more severe. These demands on material integrity in extreme environments represent the most formidable barrier to testing capability existing today.

Bibliography

Allsop, R. T., *Metallurgica,* Vol. 60, 1959, pp. 39-43, 87-92.

Barsom, J. M., "Effect of Cyclic-Stress Form on Corrosion-Fatigue Crack Propagation Below K_{Iscc} in a High-Yield-Strength Steel," presented at the International Conference on Corrosion Fatigue, University of Connecticut, Storrs, 14-18 June 1971.

Benedetti, R. L. and Creighton, D. L., *Review of Scientific Instruments,* Vol. 41, No. 4, April 1970.

Bianchi, R. A., "Survey of Evaluation of Sonic Fatigue Testing Facilities," ASDTR 61-185, March 1962.

Bucci, R. J., "Environmental Enhanced Fatigue and Stress Corrosion Cracking of a Titanium Alloy Plus a Simple Model for the Assessment of Environmental Influence on Fatigue Behavior," Del Research Corp., 1 Aug. 1970.

Burgess, J. C. and Salmon, V., "Development of a Modulated Air Stream Loudspeaker," Stanford Research Institute, Dec. 1955.

Campbell, W. E., "Fretting," *Boundary Lubrication—An Appraisal of World Literature,* Research Committee on Lubrication, American Society of Mechanical Engineers, 1969.

Clarkson, B. L. and Pietrusewicz, S. A., The University of Southampton Random Siren Facility, AASU Report 204, Dec. 1961.

Collins, J. A., "Fretting-Fatigue Damage-Factor Determination," Paper 64-WA/MD-10, American Society of Mechanical Engineers, 1964.

Comyn, R. H. and Furlani, C. W., "Fretting Corrosion," Army Material Command, Washington, D.C., Dec. 1963.

Cote, M. J., "Comparison of Approches for Sonic Fatigue Prevention," WADC ASD TDR-63-704, Sept, 1963.

Fenner, A. J. and Field, J. E., *Transactions,* North East Coast Institution of Engineers and Shipbuilders, Vol. 76, 1959-1960, p. 183.

Field, J. E., "Effect of Direction of Fretting on the Fretting-Fatigue Strength of L65 Aluminum Alloy," NEL Report 120, Oct. 1963.

Gassner, E., *On the Influence of Fretting Corrosion on the Fatigue Life of Notched Specimens of an Al-Cu-Mg 2 Alloy,* Pergamon Press, 1963.

Gray, C. L., "Study in the Use of Structural Models for Sonic Fatigue," Technical Report ASD-TR-61-547, April 1962.

Hardrath, H. F. in *Advanced Testing Techniques, ASTM STP 476,* American Society for Testing and Materials, 1970, pp. 79-95.

Harris, W. J., "The Influence of Fretting on Fatigue," AD 703 595, March 1970.

Hartman, A. and Schijve, J., *Engineering Fracture Mechanics,* Vol. 1, 1970, pp. 615-631.

Hilliard, J. K. and Fiala, W. T., "Methods of Generating Increased Sonic Power for Environmental Testing," I. E. S. 1960 Annual Convention, Los Angeles, April 1960.

Hoeppner, D. W. and Hyler, W. S., *Materials Research and Standards,* Vol. 6, No. 12, Dec. 1966.

Honeycutt, C. R. and Sawyer, J. C., "Determination at Elevated Temperature Fatigue Data on Refractory Alloys in Ultra High Vacuum," TRW CR 54203, Thompson Rame Wooldredge, Inc.

Horger, O. J., "Influence of Fretting Corrosion on the Fatigue Strength of Fitted Members," *Symposium on Fretting Corrosion, ASTM STP 144,* American Society for Testing and Materials, 1952.

Liu, H. W., Corten, H. T., and Sinclair, G. M., "Fretting Fatigue Strength of Titanium Alloy RC 130 B," *Proceedings,* American Society for Testing and Materials, Vol. 57, 1957.

Milestone, W. D., "Fatigue Analysis in Engineering Design, Fretting and Fatigue," The Dept. of Mechanical Engineering, University of Wisconsin, Madison, 18-20 Feb. 1970.

Nachtigall, A. J., Klima, S. J., Freche, J. C., and Hoffman, C. A., "The Effect of Vacuum on the Fatigue and Stress-Rupture Properties of S-816 and Income 550 at 1500°F," NASA TN D-2898, June 1965.

Plumblee, H. E. and Bartel, H. W., "Development of Expected Noise Spectra," Siren Programming Techniques and Experiment Plans for the ASD Sonic Fatigue Facility, ASD-TDR-63-674, Aug. 1963.

Rosenfeld, M. S., "Effects of Corrosion on Fatigue Life," discussion presented at 11th Annual Meeting of the International Committee on Aeronautical Fatigue, Stockholm, May 1969.

Salmen, W. J. and Gobble, L. P., "Tensile Properties of Beryllium from Room Temperature to 1600°F," 1962 Reprint, American Society for Testing and Materials, 1967.

Snowden, K. U., *Journal of Scientific Instrumentation,* Vol. 41, July 1964, p. 470.

Starkey, W. L., Marco, S. M., and Collins, J. A., "The Effect of Fretting on Fatigue Characteristics of Titanium Steel and Steel Joints," Paper 57-A-113, American Society of Mechanical Engineers, 1957.

Swanson, S. R., *Evaluating Component Fatigue Performance Under Programmed Random, and Programmed Constant Amplitude Loading,* Society of Automotive Engineers, Publication 150.07, 690050, Jan. 1969.

Swanson, S. R., "Problems in the Load-Carrying Application of High-Strength Steels," DMIC Report 210, Oct. 1964.

Teed, P. L., *Metallurgical Reviews,* Vol. 5, No. 19, 1960, pp. 267-295.

Teed, P. L., *Lubrication,* (published by Texaco, Inc.), Vol. 52, No. 4, 1966.

Thiel, C. C., "Approximate Methods of Simulating Random Noise with Pure Tone Sources," FDL-TDR-64-131, Dec. 1964.

Thiruvengadam, A., "On Corrosion Fatigue at High Frequencies," American Society for Testing and Materials, to be published.

Van Dyke, J. D., Eshleman, A., and Belcher, P. M., "Method for Designing and Testing Structures Subjected to Random Acoustic Loading," Douglas Report SM-22555-6-15-57, 1 Aug. 1956.

Winterbourne, R. E., "Researches into the Basic Mechanisms of Fretting Fatigue," Hawker Siddely D. H. Dir., Research Progress Report R245/P4/64, Oct. 1964.

Chapter 10—Structural Fatigue Testing

The discussion, so far, has been concerned largely with materials testing, in which the specimens are designed to suit the test machine frame. The test frame can be very complex or very simple, indeed. Structural testing, in which the test system must alter its form to suit the specimen, is a very popular form of test at present, especially in the area of component testing (Section 10.2).

Many of the advanced testing techniques have arisen from the development of complex aircraft structures. Thus, the following sections lean heavily on examples of aircraft applications. It should be kept in mind, however, that many of the principles and techniques are much more generally applicable. Automobiles, off-highway vehicles, bridges, buildings, power plants, and an infinite variety of other structures can utilize these methods.

There are many valid reasons for performing structural fatigue tests. Some have to do with the shortcomings of relating material fatigue behavior with structural behavior, some are concerned with the lack of accuracy in knowing the loads in individual structural elements. The greatest asset of structural testing is its ability, when performed correctly, to ferret out all the weak spots in the total design, and thereby show when and where to inspect the structure in service.

There are a number of problems associated with structural testing which have no real counterparts in materials testing, and a number of familiar problem areas which have special aspects when one considers structural testing. These can be listed partially as:

(a) *Programming*—Deciding on the degree of simulation. Programming is generally weighted toward "service" when one is dealing with practical structures.

(b) *Program Control*—In structural testing, the simultaneous action of several load inputs is a new problem to the test engineer familiar only with single-channel testing. To make all inputs or channels respond in unison or to a master program can involve a great deal of work and many phase control problems.

(c) *Gripping*—In structural testing, there is a need for adapting the gripping to the specimen, while in materials testing one adapts the specimen to the gripping. Often, multiple grip straps are used, which must diffuse their loads realistically into the structure.

(*d*) *Fail-Safe*—The prevention of inadvertent loading is all-important in structural testing. Section 10.3 is devoted to this problem.

(*e*) *The Degree of "Fixity" in the Specimen*—For some structures, floating the structure on the loading system or hanging it from the loading system is required for correct simulation of the fatigue loadings. For other cases, part of the specimen may be firmly bolted to a reaction frame. Often the structure will be placed in a non-normal (for example, inverted) position for the test.

(*f*) *The Test Environment*—Shrouding a specimen in a materials test with a special atmosphere is often a simple matter. Heating and cooling the surfaces of a full size supersonic transport is quite another matter in terms of cost and complexity.

(*g*) *Accuracy of Loading*—A number of the previous factors make the accuracy of loading difficult to assess.

(*h*) *Program Supervision*—One must establish whether it is desirable (or even possible) for a structural test to be monitored manually, or if due to sheer complexity one must rely on automation [*36*].

(*i*) *Failure Criteria*—For many structures, fracture is too simplistic a concept for failure. Often, just finding where "failure" is occurring can be a problem.

(*j*) *Dependability*—Multiple channel testing with multiple coordinated elements of programming control and readout make dependability a problem. "Down-time" in structural testing is nearly always a severe strain on the budget.

(*k*) *Test Cost*—Structural testing is very often expensive. Since, however, it alone bridges whatever gaps there are between analysis and reality, it is usually worth the considerable expense involved.

Figure 84 illustrates the cost of full-scale testing in Great Britain, and underlines the great expense that these represent [*37*]. Similar trends would be observed in North America.

Despite these high costs, the correlation between the test results and actual service experience has not always been very good. Fortunately, the trend is to better correlation in recent years.

10.1 Programming Information

Programming for structural testing is nearly always variable-amplitude (unless the service condition is constant-amplitude) because there have been many cases reported where failures have occurred at non-typical locations in the structure when loaded with constant amplitude cycles. Generally, the larger the test piece, the more likely that digital techniques are used, in contrast to analog loadings (noise, magnetic tapes, function generators) for components. Fatigue test loadings for full-scale aircraft for

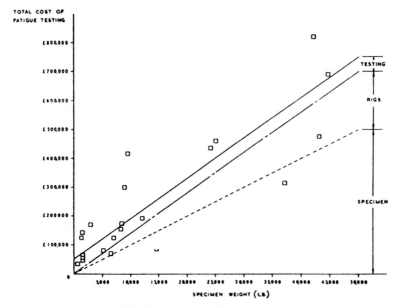

FIG. 84—*Total cost of fatigue testing.*

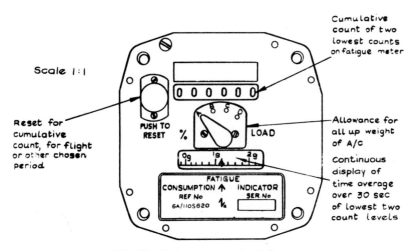

FIG. 85—*Fatigue consumption indicator.*

example, are essentially determinate in that care is taken to follow a predetermined sequence of loadings within a small error band [*38-41*].

In structural testing, therefore, the major problem is to establish a reasonable loading spectrum. There are several types of devices available to provide the input for the spectrum. These devices include the following generic types.

Direct Loading Meters

These devices (for example, Fig. 85), typically involving accelerometers and counters, are used to monitor the number of times various levels of acceleration are exceeded. In this way an (accumulated) load spectrum is developed.

Strain Level Counters [42]

These devices are similar to loading meters but utilize strain in a structural element to trigger the level counters as described in Ref 12.

10.2 Full-Scale Fatigue Testing

Because large structures involve large strokes, large loads, and slow speeds in applying the loads, they are usually tested using hydraulic actuators.

One aspect of structural fatigue testing which should not be overlooked is the near impossibility of simulating all vehicle dynamics in a stationary test facility. Aircraft and automobiles, for example, travel at high velocities and their service use represents a tremendous amount of kinetic energy. Simulation, to be feasible at all, must apply to the effects of such energy rather than simulation of the energy itself. Sometimes, there are exceptions as with automobile tires, where dynamic differences can be too great to be neglected, and one should simulate loading by having the tire rotating during the test.

In moving from cause to effect in simulating loads one must be consistent in the location at which loads are recorded in service, and the point at which test loads are applied. For example, it is almost impossible to simulate wheel axle load histories by applying loads through the tire.

For accuracy, speed of programming, and synchronization of many signals, the digital programming devices are currently most popular. Whether the digital equipment includes a computer or a special programmer, such as a block programmer, depends usually on the number of channels involved.

Paper tape programmers are often used for multiple-channel testing. While the tapes made from ordinary paper do wear out quickly when repeatedly cycled, nylon aluminized or Mylar tapes can be very rugged and, with photoelectric readers, have negligible wear problems.

There are a number of details associated with any structural test involving electrohydraulics that are of the nature of "good housekeeping." These following details are not only important for the best use of the test fixtures, but for safety as well.

1. Avoid situations where hydraulic lines are rubbing against hard surfaces as they flex back and forth due to the loading changes. Such abrasive action can cause dangerous ruptures.
2. Capacitance balance in long transducer leads when using alternating current excitation can lead to structural testing inaccuracies. This condition is fairly easily remedied by adding capacitive bridge balancing circuits to the system.
3. In structural testing certain parts of the structure (for example, tips of a wing) are required to undergo larger displacements in the same time than other sections. Careful consideration must, therefore, be given to flow control to avoid operational problems.
4. Two jacks operating at different frequencies, for example, nacelle jack 3.6 times as fast as basic wing loading frequency will present interaction difficulties. It is best to use exact multiples, if possible.
5. Complete dead-weight counterbalancing structure is often more desirable than applying tare load through the jacks. However, there are friction problems, and the response can be very slow due to the inertia of the system. For example, even at only 10 cpm, inertia load errors can be 1 percent of the loading. The friction problems can often be handled by determining the friction loads, and adjusting the driving loads accordingly. Loading above and below eliminates compression jacks (Fig. 86). Multiple jacks can simulate simultaneously the action of wing spanwise and chordwise loading and torque by differential loading. Often, one jack will be used to load several

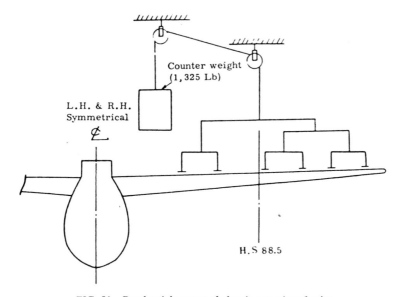

FIG. 86—*Dead-weight counterbalancing an aircraft wing.*

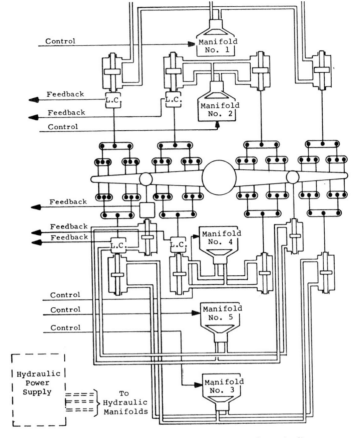

FIG. 87—*Small aircraft structures test system, schematic diagram.*

points on the structure through the use of "whiffletrees" (Fig. 87), a term borrowed from the horse-and-buggy days, when a single connection to the buggy was distributed to two horses by means of a transverse bar.

6. Another problem that can develop in full scale testing, is the change in load alignment as the specimen deforms. Since the specimen, such as parts of an aircraft wing, can change their angular position by as much as 40 deg under loading, some allowance must be made to provide correct simulation at all angles. This is often a problem not only with loading jacks but the tare weight counterbalance system as well. The problem is further complicated by the incorporation of variable sweep in high performance aircraft.

7. One of the more significant problems in using more than one actuator in a single test is interaction or "cross-talk." Cross-talk is

simply the unwanted presence of a signal from another actuator system on a given actuator system. Cross-talk can occur in at least three different modes, the mechanical linkage, the hydraulic fluid, and the electronics used to drive the hydraulic actuators. Another type of spurious transfer is called cross coupling and is discussed in Ref *43*.

8. Full size structural testing is an area where zero "error" is economically impossible. Accuracy limits, however, should be determined. For example, load accuracy can be determined by using load cells traceable to the National Bureau of Standards. This is the absolute accuracy of the load.

9. The speed of the test is often limited mainly by the accuracy desired, and in every structural test some compromise is achieved on this point. Generally, a 2 percent accuracy on mean load and 2 percent accuracy on the dynamic alternating load (provided it is above a threshold value) are considered satisfactory criteria.

Because of the problems associated with establishing damage equivalence in fatigue from one type of loading to another, the Flight-by-Flight approach, where the programming simulates all the essential aspects of a complete flight mission in sequence, before moving on to the next "flight," is the favorite approach used today.

The testing of full-scale structures usually involves the in-phase action of several actuators, each with an appropriately sized load cell connected in series with it (or a calibrated differential pressure transducer). It is important that the load cell connected to a given actuator be "matched" so that the cell is operating in its optimum range for maximum accuracy. Also, the actuator itself should be "sized," so that it is operating near its limits under full loading at that station. This not only ensures economy of operation, but the least weight will usually be associated with the fastest frequency response. Further, from a fail-safe standpoint, matching the maximum load closely will prevent the actuator from having the capability (if it malfunctions) of applying appreciably greater loads and destroying an expensive specimen.

When a full-scale test is being planned, there are two different approaches the planners may take with regard to supervision of the test.

The "Test Director" Approach—In this approach, the test director acts much like a seasoned airline captain, "flying" his structure through the tests. Great pains are taken to provide significant information to him at all times through data acquisition and display. Continuous indications on monitor cathode-ray-tube (CRT) screens of the variations between the requested program and the actual load levels, the ability to play back the last few minutes of a test when something abnormal occurs, and a wide variety of visual indicators are part of this approach.

The Automated Approach—In this approach every effort is made to automate the test so that the required direct supervision is of a much lesser "grade" than that in test director approach. Emergency actions are worked out before-hand so that there is (ideally) no need for quick thinking at the time of an abnormality.

A number of basic "truths" about large-scale structural fatigue tests have been listed which are worth repeating here.

1. Fatigue tests take a long time to run.
2. Fatigue tests are (usually) not scheduled as early as possible.
3. Major ground tests almost always experience failures (short of the anticipated service life).
4. Structural redesigns often delay major ground tests.
5. A single fatigue test is not optimum and (even) second tests are seldom conducted.

Fatigue testing of *full-size assemblies* has become fairly common for applications requiring highly-efficient light-weight structures [44]. In addition to defining the fatigue strength of the structure for the specific conditions of loading, this type of test provides a proof test of the assumptions made during structural design. Tests of full-scale assemblies include the influences of numerous structural interactions between the various component parts. Because of the wide variety of requirements, testing devices of this type normally are custom made for the specific class of application.

10.2.1. Resonant Systems for Complete Structures

In the interest of minimizing the cost of equipment and the power required, resonant systems are frequently used. The structural specimen may be mounted in a jig, masses attached so that the response to the exciting force produces the appropriate distribution of static and dynamic stresses. Dynamic forces are introduced by rotating eccentrics, crack-actuated springs, electromagnetic shakers, or slipping-clutch devices. The rotating eccentrics are frequently counter-rotating to eliminate all forces except those in the desired direction. Others have been built with two sets of counter-rotating masses, but with the phase relation between the sets adjustable while the unit is in motion. This latter feature allows starting with a minimum transient with low torque and also facilitates programming the load. Resonant techniques are usually limited to the simulation of stress levels at a relatively small number of locations. This fact may represent a severe limitation to their use in the testing of large structures.

10.2.2. Acoustic Excitation

Tests to evaluate the resistance to failure due to acoustic vibrations in structural components are an important phase of aeronautical structural design. Representative portions of structures are subjected to acoustic excitation. The excitation is frequently provided by a siren whose frequency can be adjusted to match a resonant frequency in the structure and then held to produce continuous vibrations. Usually, several modes of vibration are excited simultaneously in service and simulation is improved if a random excitation is employed. Special variable-frequency sirens and jet exhaust have been employed to provide such excitation. This method is generally limited to tests of panels and local structure. Correlations with service failure are strictly empirical.

10.2.3. Structural Fatigue Testing with Concurrent Thermal Cycling

Reference 45 gives a detailed description of the sophisticated test system required for the simultaneous thermal- and mechanical-load duty cycle for a supersonic transport (the Concorde). The thermal and mechanical duty cycles are shown in Fig. 88 and suggests the complexities that confront the test engineering staff in devising the experimental facility, Fig. 89. These complexities are present even if the test under consideration is to be conducted on a component.

Controlling the thermal and mechanical duty cycles can best be accomplished by computer facilities. The principles of computer control and monitoring for the Concorde fatigue test are diagrammed in Fig. 90. A sample of the logic structure for the same fatigue test is shown in Fig. 91.

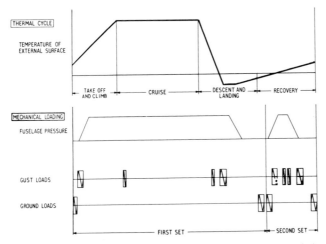

FIG. 88—*Thermal cycle and mechanical loading in accelerated test cycle (Ref 45).*

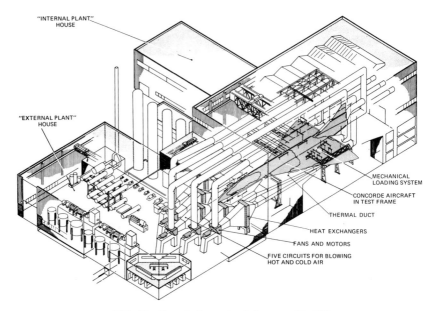

FIG. 89—*Test rig for major fatigue test* (*Ref* 45).

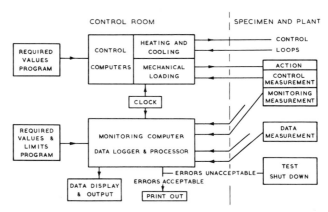

FIG. 90—*Principles of control and monitoring system* (*Ref* 45).

10.2.4. Monitoring Fatigue Damage in Structural Tests

In full-scale tests there are a number of aspects to the problem of damage monitoring in addition to those discussed in Chapter 8. One of the main differences in structural testing is that quite often one does not really know where damage will begin. With this is coupled the problem that, under certain conditions, failure (due to a build-up of fatigue

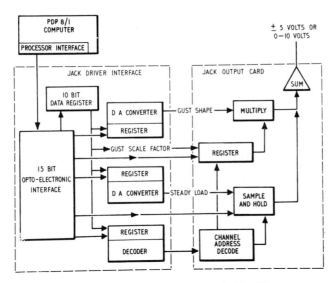

FIG. 91—*Loading computer system* (*Ref* 45).

damage) can occur suddenly, and involve forces making the failure a very hazardous situation for personnel in the vicinity of the test.

Crack Location—The periodic inspection of structures by nondestructive testing (NDT) techniques (X-ray, ultrasonics, etc.) is often used but involves interrupting the test program and testing the structure when it is motionless. These methods are outside the scope of this manual since they are essentially after-the-fact methods. While some of the NDT methods can, in principle, be used while a test is in progress, this approach has been prohibitively expensive.

The sound emitted by cracking elements in a structure and detected by the human ear can often help in tracing the location of cracks. Acoustic emission techniques (discussed earlier) can be applied during the testing and have shown promise for future applications. The main problem is currently one of distinguishing the signal from background noise.

Spotting the crack location early has many useful advantages. For example, minor modifications then can be made on the production line, compared with extensive changes when a large sector is involved. Also, knowledge of crack initiation time is important in the setting of inspection intervals.

Preventing Catastrophic Failures of Structures—One of the approaches common in the 1950's and 1960's in aircraft fatigue testing, involving pressurization cycles of the fuselage, was to keep the pressurized structure fully immersed in water. This avoided the explosive release of the pneumatic energy build-up that air pressurization would develop when a crack attained critical proportions.

Lately, however, testing in air (with many precautions for personnel protection) has been generally accepted as the more desirable mode. One of the reasons for this decision is that one cannot easily assess the corrosion effects associated with water testing. Also, the ability to inspect structures under water is never really as good as it can be in air.

For testing in air, the object is to make the volume of air being compressed as small as possible. This can be accomplished (as it was on the Boeing 727) by filling the fuselage as much as possible with large pieces of foam material to displace most of the air. This will tend to defuse the specimen by drastically lowering the energy available for catastrophic failure.

10.3 Fatigue Testing of Components

Component testing (Fig. 92) is intended to evaluate the fatigue strength of a machine part, structure, or a complete assembly under service environment, taking into consideration design and fabrication factors not represented in simple test specimens. The types of test pieces used in component or structural testing are varied. They may mock up structural details which can be evaluated prior to the manufacture of a complex structural assembly. Procedures are dictated by the special service conditions, so that uniform practices cannot be established for this type of testing. To have any value in predicting serviceability from component tests, both preparation of test pieces and testing environment should be arranged to simulate as nearly as possible the conditions of service so that laboratory failures are similar to the service failures. Because of their very diversified and specialized nature, uniform practices in the design and preparation of component test pieces cannot be included in this chapter (Fig. 93).

Component parts are normally fatigue tested in a manner representative of anticipated service loading. In general, the stress distribution induced in the component part can vary considerably with position. Hence, the fatigue strength of the particular component, including the effects of the variables induced by the manufacturing process, is evaluated rather than basic material strength. Normally, experimental stress analysis techniques are required to define stress states in complex components.

10.3.1 Forced Vibration Systems for Components

Many electronic and mechanical devices used in aircraft and missiles are subjected to a vibration test to prove they will operate in a vibrating environment. Usually, the frequency of vibration is "swept" through a specified range and then allowed to "dwell" at a frequency at which a resonant response is indentified. Failure to survive such a test is usually due to a fatigue failure, so that in a sense, a fatigue test has been

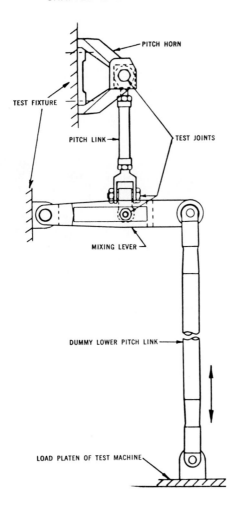

FATIGUE TEST SETUP

FIG. 92—*An example of a component fatigue test for a helicopter part.*

conducted. Machines for conducting such tests may be actuated mechanically, electromechanically, or hydraulically. Tests are sometimes conducted with a random vibration of the test article.

10.4 Fail-Safe Aspects

Here, the term fail-safe refers to protection of the test piece from malfunctions in the testing system.

FIG. 93—*The fatigue loading of an automobile suspension.*

Failure recognition is a key factor in any fail-safe decision. It is for this reason that tests are run with a great number of signals which would appear to the outsider as redundant or superfluous. For example, an actuator operating in load feedback control may have a second load cell bridge being monitored, a pressure transducer in its cylinder, and a deflection or stroke transducer monitoring its travel. Such redundancy, however, greatly aids the director in recognizing a problem, by observing which signal begins to deviate first. Since a single fatigue test may run for several weeks, the investment in the test is considerable and the fail-safe aspects become of great economic importance.

Fail-Safe

Many testing situations utilize combined hold and dump criteria, such as: (a) if the loading exceeds ±2 percent of desired value, switch to "hold," and (b) if the loading exceeds ±10 percent error, switch to "dump."

There are three basic sources of trouble in modern structural test systems.

1. The electronic aspects.
2. The hydraulics.
3. The mechanical aspects.

In the event of a malfunction in a large structural test system, corrective action must be taken quickly to prevent, in some cases, an economic disaster for the company carrying out the test. The answer, of course, is to anticipate every possibility of malfunction, and to "preset" an appropriate remedy.

Hold Remedies

In a situation where, for example, a long actuator is almost fully extended and a reversing signal is achieved, there may be the possibility of a slight misalignment to cause the actuator to "cock," preventing any further movement back in the retracting direction. The test system would observe that the load is going outside limits in a direction indicative of such a condition, and would call for a "hold" on all other channels until the test director can take over manually, and unload the cocked actuator by studying the logic of the test situation. Note, that an automatic decision to "dump" or "ramp to zero" would be disastrous in this situation since the actuator in trouble would be loaded further, probably resulting in destruction of the local test structure, or the actuator, or both.

Dump Remedies

On the other hand, consider the case where many actuators are pulling a large specimen in a tension mode. Suddenly, due to a malfunction of the electronics, one of the actuators is inadvertently commanded to go "hard over" (usually at maximum speed). Here, however, if the system were instructed to "hold," the inadvertent command would not be cancelled and the actuator could destroy the local area of the specimen involved in its attachment. Such malfuntions generally occur too fast for human intervention. There have been a number of ingenious remedies used to prevent such overload.

The Use of Yield Strips

In this remedy, the actuator is connected to the specimen with a strip of metal attached in series between the two elements. The metal is selected so that its yield behavior approximates the classical elastic-plastic behavior. That is, when yield is passed, the strip will deform greatly and quickly, so that no load greater than yield can be applied in tension. This remedy is very good, since it is not dependent on any mechanical or electrical control devices associated with the actuator.

Pilot-Operated Check Valves

It is frequently desired to incorporate fail-safe devices in structural loading systems whereby hydraulic actuators are locked in position upon

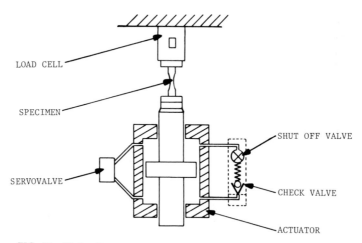

LOAD CELL

SPECIMEN

SHUT OFF VALVE

SERVOVALVE

CHECK VALVE

ACTUATOR

FIG. 94—*Hydraulic actuator incorporating the use of a check valve.*

receiving a fail-safe signal. Since pilot-operated checkvalves are simple, low cost devices, they are often used in this service and are connected as shown in Fig. 94. In order to lock the actuator, a master solenoid valve is closed removing pressure from the pilot section of the check valves and allowing the valves to seat. The valves are necessarily oriented such that they prevent flow from *leaving* the actuator and thus do not prevent flow from entering the actuator. In many structural installations, actuators having large diameter rods, with respect to the piston diameter, are frequently used. Referring to Fig. 94, it may be seen that flow into the fixed end of the piston could develop maximum system pressure in this cavity. To be conservative, it must be assumed that the maximum pressure on the rod end of the cylinder is equivalent to the system pressure times the area ratio. Thus, with an area ratio of three and a supply pressure of 3000 psi, a pressure of 9000 psi would be developed in the rod end of the actuator. Since most hydraulic components have a maximum safe working pressure of one and one-half times the normal working pressure, it may be seen that the component working ratings and often the burst pressure rating as well can be exceeded.

A second problem relates to the speed of response in systems incorporating check valves of this type. It should be noted that the valves are locked upon removal of pilot pressure and that a substantial volume of oil must be pushed from the pilot piston chamber for the valve to seat. In ordinary installations, relatively long pilot lines are required, resulting in fluid friction with pressure drops opposing the flow of oil from the pilot piston chamber. It is not unusual to expect delays in excess of 100 ms under these circumstances. Where specimen spring rates are rather soft and valves are sized to the flow requirements, this will not result in large load errors. However, in cases where the spring rate is high and a large valve is used, significant overloading can occur in the interval of time it takes for the check valves to seat.

Both of these problems are avoided by the use of electrically operated solenoid valves which have a high response and which prevent flow of fluid in both directions.

Anti-Compression Valves—The anti-compression valve is a device that may be incorporated into the actuator manifold on fatigue test systems. It is intended to protect the load cell, actuator, grips, and specimen from damage that might result from an operator inadvertently applying a compressive load to a specimen designed for tension only. It has a valve for locking it out when compression loads are to be applied.

The check valve used has a back pressure spring that is adjusted to allow up to about 2 percent of full actuator force to facilitate test setup.

Hydraulic Load Limiters—Hydraulic load limiters provide a fail-safe limiting level of hydraulic actuator tensile and compressive loading in fatigue test systems. Basically, the load limiter valve is a differential relief valve with capability of operating with different area ratio actuators, to permit (*a*) complete passive fail-safe operation independent of any related electrical or mechanical components, (*b*) full flow response exceeding that of typical servovalves, (*c*) both tension and compression load limits individually adjustable with no interaction, and (*d*) convenient interchangeable parts to match most common actuator area ratios.

References

[36] Wood, H. A., "The Air Force Airplane Structural Integrity Program," ASTM Committee E-9, Air Force Flight Dynamics Lab., (FDTR) Wright-Patterson AFB, Ohio.
[37] Harpur, N. F. and Troughton, A. J., "The Value of Full Scale Fatigue Testing," private communication.
[38] Ito, M., P2V-7 Fatigue Test Report, Japan Defense Army Technical Research and Development Institute.
[39] Harpur, N. F., Discussion to paper by Gassner and Schuetz in *Fatigue Evaluation of Aircraft Structures*, Pergamon Press.
[40] Cowgill, L. C., *The Aeronautical Journal of the Royal Aeronautical Society*, Vol. 74, July 1970, pp. 559-572.
[41] Kamiyama, T. T., Kazuyuki, S. F., and Kitatani, K., "Full Scale Fatigue Test of Twin Turboprop Transport."
[42] Weiss, D. E., "Strain Level Counter for Monitoring Aircraft Fatigue," presented at the Oct. 1970 Meeting of the Instrument Society of America, Aerospace Instrumentation Division.
[43] Larson, R. L. and Swanson, S. R., "Random Load Testing with Multiple Inputs," presented at International Conference on Mechanical Behavior of Materials, Kyoto, Japan, 15-20 Aug. 1971.
[44] Rosenfeld, M. S. in *Testing for Prediction of Material Performance in Structures and Components, ASTM STP 515*, American Society for Testing and Materials, 1972, pp. 285-313.

[45] Ripley, E. L., "The Philosophy of Structural Testing a Supersonic Transport Aircraft with Particular Reference to the Influence of the Thermal Cycle," Royal Aircraft Establishment, RAE Ref. Structures YSE/C/010.

Chapter 11—Automated Fatigue Testing

Undoubtedly, the most fascinating development in the field of fatigue testing has been the recent growth of automation in this area. Fatigue tests by their very nature are very tedious to monitor continuously, and yet modern demands for complex signal simulation often do not permit one to use the elementary and easy-to-monitor signals so widely used in the past.

Computer involvement in fatigue testing is nearly always associated with a servo-system to check the feedback against the command signal. The combined action of computer programming and a feedback servo system permits testing under computer control. This is, of course, one (large) step further than using the computer merely for data acquisition.

The areas of fatigue testing which presently benefit from automation the most, are the fields of low-cycle fatigue (with accumulation of fatigue damage) [46] and multi-channel structural testing.

The application of computer control of complex stress-strain programs is made even more useful by the ability of the computer to analyze the data [47]. Fatigue damage analysis can be conducted and life predictions can be made. These abilities and techniques then make possible the simulation and and evaluation of complex real-life fatigue conditions.

A real-time system is one that works with and acts upon data that are being generated. This, of course, requires that the computer be linked with transducers or devices capable of obtaining data and generating useful output. In both acquiring data and providing action, the computer must be "interfaced" with peripheral devices [48]. To provide pacing for the interface components, a timing section is included. The timing section controls the intervals between data samples and the rate at which the system acts. Figure 95 shows a block diagram of a typical computer and interface system.

One of the most interesting questions raised in using computer control for dynamic testing is: what kind of computer to use? From the experience accumulated to date, the on-line capability of the minicomputer and the generally modest (to a computer) demands of dynamic testing, point to the use of the minicomputer as an integral part of the test system independent of other computer requirements [49]. For certain

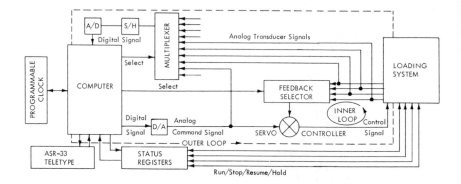

FIG. 95—*Simplified system block diagram—digital computer/analog servo controller.*

applications, the multiplexing of signals can result in the simultaneous control of several test machines from a single minicomputer.

This chapter describes the essential features of digital computer control, analog computer control, and some brief discussion of hybird systems. Listed are some examples of software programs developed for the the two fields of fatigue just mentioned, followed by a description of some problems associated with data acquisition. Some brief notes on computer applications for structural testing are also included.

11.1 Computer Control

In a conventional testing system without a computer, the transducer (readout) signals are not communicated to the function generation equipment. If decisions are to be made based on how the test is proceeding, an operator must monitor readout, make the appropriate decisions, and manually take the required action. In a computerized system, the computer both generates the servocontroller command and gathers test data. This allows it to make decisions and alter the test based upon how the test is proceeding. Figure 95 shows how this is done. The inner loop consists of the servo controller driving a servo-valve in the loading system with the selected transducer feedback signal closing the loop. The outer loop (dotted line) includes the computer and its interface with an analog command signal to the servo controller closing the loop. With the inner loop controlling strain, for example, the outer loop can be controlling complex parameters such as the product of stress and strain. The outer loop can change the analog command signal, based on its own decisions, any time during the test [50].

Computer-controlled fatigue testing thus permits on-line continuous control with the added capability (when carefully programmed) of making on-line decisions based on both instantaneous, and accumulative information [51].

These capabilities are of great value in tests such as cumulative damage studies (for example, Ref 52), tests involving mode switching such as in changing from strain-controlled cycles to load-controlled creep, Neuber control for studies of notched parts (see Ref 53), and other tests involving either continuously-computed parameters or decisions based on the data being generated.

A typical example of a digital computer incorporated into a fatigue test system is shown in Fig. 96. In most computer-controlled fatigue testing systems presently in use, the feedback (transducer) system is essentially analog, and the servocontroller is also analog in form (Fig. 96). Consequently, the digital computer must operate through buffers.

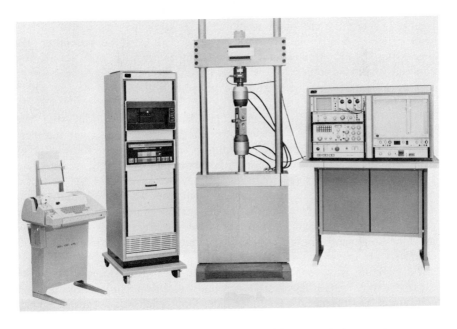

FIG. 96—A typical test system utilizing its own minicomputer in its operation.

It is conceivable that in the future, all-digital test systems will be built, in which digital transducers and servo controllers are incorporated to avoid this conversion problem. However, no such systems exist as yet.

To run a computer-controlled test, operator/computer interaction is necessary. The operator usually indicates the test through a teletype (Fig. 96) and the input information (see Section 11.2) is input to the computer.

The computer through the proper interface devices, initiates programs, when directed, in each of the channels as preprogrammed.

11.2 Programming

The extent of programming in computer-controlled fatigue testing is presently almost a matter of personal taste. Skilled software programmers tend to overuse software to the exclusion, sometimes, of simple hardware subsystems (for example, digital filtering, etc.). Skilled engineers, on the other hand, tend to insert mechanical devices whenever possible, minimizing the sophistication of the software.

The key to making an operational system is appropriate programming. Programming for a real time system varies from conventional programming in that it must be able to take care of interruptions.

An interruption to the system is a signal that one of the interface devices needs attention. For instance, when the analog-to-digital converter has finished converting, it will signal the computer to indicate an action is required. When the computer recognizes this service signal, it will initiate appropriate action to get the converted signal into the computer for processing. Some devices will have a higher priority and should be serviced ahead of others. This means that the computer will have to sample all interrupt signals and the program will have to decide which device will be serviced first.

Because of these critical timing problems, it is essential that the programs used for control purposes operate in the most efficient manner. For this reason, no matter what techniques are used, precise knowledge of programming limitations is required. For example, because of its intent to provide a general language, FORTRAN may be too slow for the response time requirements of a servo system—but the use of FORTRAN to assemble programs in machine language may be possible. Certainly, any technique that is used may require the programmer to review the machine-language program to ensure that the maximum speed and efficiency are present.

To generate these sophisticated techniques, a programmer should be utilized who is familiar with not only real-time programming and computers, but the fatigue test operation. Only when this programmer has a knowledge of fatigue testing will he be able to command the automated system to generate meaningful material tests.

A sample listing of fatigue test software programs is given in Section 11.4.

11.3 Interfacing a Computer with a Fatigue Test System

The interface system required between the computer and the test machine must be designed with regard to the type of testing the automated system is to perform. Although computer manufacturers do have

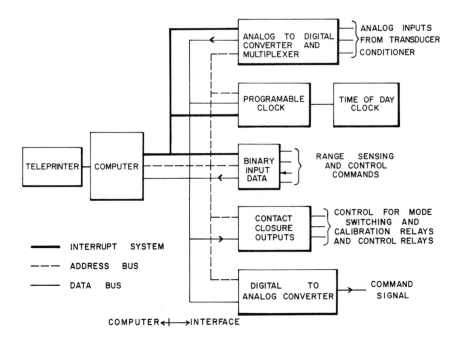

FIG. 97—*System block diagram for computer interface networks.*

standard interface packages, their use for specific applications must be examined carefully.

Basically, the interfacing should consist of the devices necessary for the computer to converse with the test machine (a digital-to-analog system); devices for the test system to relay information to the computer (an analog-to-digital converter); and a system whereby the computer can control a test through peripheral devices. Figure 97 is a block diagram showing a typical interface system.

Based upon the information obtained from the test variables being monitored and the test program, the computer will supply a command signal to the analog-to-digital converter and, hence, to the test system controller.

This command signal should have enough resolution to provide a continuous command function rather than a series of step functions. Therefore, the resolution of the D/A converter should be greater than the system resolution. The derived analog signal also should be free of noise so as not to introduce errors into the control system.

The analog-to-digital system used to convert the transducer analog information to a digital signal capable of being used by the processor must possess certain characteristics particularly with respect to resolution and speed. Modern analog-to-digital (A/D) converters are capable of working to speeds of 10 000 conversions per second and faster with an accuracy of 0.1 percent of full-scale or better.

Although high speed analog-to-digital converters that will accept low-level inputs (that is, 50 mV) are available, devices that accept a 10-V full-scale high level signal are generally preferred because they offer higher noise immunity.

Peripheral devices should contain contact closures addressable by the computer to permit such functions as mode switching (for example, load to strain), calibration relays (for prior-to-testing system checkout) and control (high/low and on/off pressure).

An example of a typical low-cycle fatigue test would be where the maximum strain levels are controlled to some random limit. After the operator had loaded or called into the processor memory the proper program, entered the test identification, maximum and minimum strain limits along with the desired strain rate, and inserted the specimen into the load frame grips, the test would be ready to run. When the extensometers were zeroed and the run switch depressed, the computer would calculate a normalized random number and factor the maximum strain limit by this number. The load frame would be commanded to load the specimen until this random strain limit was achieved. The rate at which the specimen was loaded would be controlled by the rate entered in the test setup.

After the specimen completed one cycle at the first random strain level, the computer would calculate a second normalized number and factor the maximum strain limit again. The load frame would continue to cycle the specimen between the random strain limits until it failed. Various techniques can be used in the program for generating random numbers. Using different formulas it is possible to obtain groups of random numbers with different power spectral densities.

After each half cycle, the processor calculates the energy expended for that period and outputs that information on the teleprinter along with the random stress level, strain level, and a consecutive count of the number of half cycles. When the specimen fails, the teleprinter summarizes the total number of stress reversals, the total energy expended in the test, the average reversal strain, and the root mean square of the reversal strains. A typical printout of such data and calculations is shown in Fig. 98.

Using Computers for Structural Testing

In structural testing using computer control, there are several important stages which, due to the complexity of the overall picture, should be considered separately.

Dry Runs—Stepping through the required program at both slow speed and at maximum anticipated speed electronically (without hydraulic power) is very advisable. It should be possible to run the program either

I.D.: ASTM-R2
Random: 1
Strain Limit: .0076
Strain Rate: .015
Diameter: .498

Point No.	Stress Value	Strain Value	Energy H Cycle (lbs-in/in ↑3)
0001	+.4491E+05	+.4958E-02	+.1980E+02
0002	-.8606E+04	-.3663E-02	+.2292E+02
0003	+.3834E+05	+.4030E-02	+.1210E+02
0004	-.4088E+05	-.5056E-02	+.4802E+02
0005	+.4617E+05	+.6155E-02	+.9906E+02
0006	-.4211E+05	-.5446E-02	+.9256E+02
0008	-.1602E+05	-.2833E-02	+.5837E+01
0009	+.4266E+05	+.4665E-02	+.4760E+02
0010	-.4356E+05	-.6277E-02	+.1002E+03
3660	-.3649E+05	-.3859E-02	+.4476E+02
3661	+.4103E+05	+.5446E-02	+.5899E+02
3662	-.4298E+05	-.5740E-02	+.1006E+03
3664	-.3353E+05	-.4127E-02	+.2867E+02
3666	-.4133E+05	-.5373E-02	+.5747E+02
3667	+.4341E+05	+.6717E-02	+.1495E+03
3668	-.4484E+05	-.6888E-02	+.1723E+03

Number of Reversals = 3668
Total Energy = +.1818E+06
Average Strain = +.3866E-02
RMS Peaks = +.4449E-02
RMS = +.2567E-02

FIG. 98—*Random low-cycle fatigue data.*

in the smoothly running continuous mode, or to move through the program step by step for examination.

Slow Startup—In most full-scale systems, there are strong reasons for beginning a test (especially with a very expensive specimen) using some form of slow startup. It is generally agreed that the effect of frequency is small, while the effect of amplitude is large. Consequently, the slow startup should (ideally) use full amplitude values from the beginning, but with one-tenth, say, the normal operating frequency.

Closing the Loop—The tolerances associated with closing the feedback loop in a structural test are much more critical, since in many cases the loads are the end result of many actuators moving in concert through different ranges of load and displacement simultaneously. Extra features in test equipment used to cater to this problem are often referred to as "pacing devices."

Generally, the endpoints in any unit segment of a structural test program are the most critical. For achieving these levels, the channels or actuators that arrive there first, are instructed to "hold" while the others catch up. When all channels have "arrived," the next step is undertaken in a similar manner. The adherence to the commanded path from the beginning point to the end point is usually not as critical. For example a tolerance (error) of less than 1 percent of range may be specified for the end point, while a tolerance of ±2 percent may be adequate for the load versus time history between levels.

11.4 Digital Fatigue Test Program Software

A listing of typical software programs used in computer controlled fatigue testing is given in this section. The four main areas of computer-controlled fatigue testing are:

(*a*) constant amplitude fatigue (Programs 1,2),
(*b*) random amplitude fatigue (Programs 3,5),
(*c*) low cycle fatigue (Programs 4,5), and
(*d*) spectrum loading fatigue (Program 6).

Software Program 1—Digital Function Generator

Abstract

This program produces sine, haversine, ramp, or square waves command signals (Fig. 99). Although not intended to replace analog, or digital function generators, this program will, in many instances, provide the same flexibility and, in other cases, provide greater flexibility.

In the ramp rate mode 1 to 100 levels and rates may be defined. Therefore, tests that require multi-rates and levels or arbitrary waveforms can be performed. The slowest rise time from zero to full scale is approximately 40 000 s or more than 120 h. The fastest rise time from zero to full scale is 0.409 s.

In the sine and haversine mode the fastest rate is in excess of 100 Hz and the slowest rate is approximately one cycle per 150 or 0.4 cpm.

In the square wave mode the fastest rate is 500 Hz and the slowest rate is approximately 0.25 Hz.

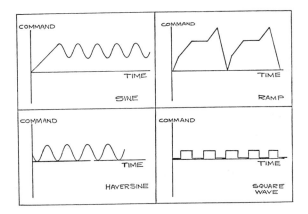

FIG. 99—*Typical fatigue programs for repeated-waveform loading.*

Input Parameters

1. The mode of feedback control.
2. Type of function: sine, haversine, ramp, or square wave.
3. If sine or haversine:
    (a) mean level,
    (b) amplitude,
    (c) cycles/second, and
    (d) number of cycles.
4. If ramp:
    (a) number of ramps,
    (b) command level and time in seconds to that level for each ramp, and
    (c) number of cycles.
5. If square wave:
    (a) amplitude, and
    (b) cycles/second.

Data Output

1. Number of cycles on the specimen.

Sample Data Input

Function generation for sine, haversine, ramp and square waves

load, ext., stroke, aux: 20,10,4,2
Id:Ted
Control:Strain
Function:Ramp

No. of Ramps (Max=100):4
Level(%), Time (Sec):: 10,40.

$\leftarrow$40,,,

Rate too fast
No of Ramps (Max=100):2
Level (%), Time (Sec):: 10,20,10,20,
No Cycles: 1,

Ready
Be

Function generation for sine,haversine,ramp and square waves

Control:ext
Function:Ramp
No of Ramps (max=100):8
Level (%),Time (Sec):: 20,50,30,.5,40,10,50,.5,60,10,70,.5,80,10,90,.5,
No Cycles:1
Ready
Be

Function generation for sine,haversine,ramp and square waves

Ready
Be

Load,ext,stroke,aux:20,10,4,2,
Id:Ted
Control:Load
Function:Sine
Mean (%),Amp (%),Rate (HZ):::10,50,6,
No Cycles:50,
Ready

Software Program 2—Fatigue

This program is written for both high-cycle fatigue and low-cycle fatigue applications (Fig. 100). The program may be run in either load control or strain control and use either a sine wave or a triangle wave as the command.

Parameter Inputs

1. Mode of control is either load or strain.
2. Type of wave form is either sine or triangle.
3. Which cycle to calculate the slope (note that the slope is always calculated for the first cycle.)

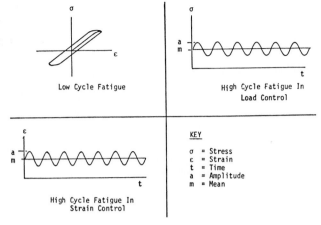

FIG. 100—*High-cycle and low-cycle fatigue programs.*

Sample Data Input

Random Low Cycle Fatigue
Range Constants:
20000,1000,4000,2000,.05,.05,.05,.05,
Date :Tes←14 Feb 70
I.D. :Test Demo
Random :No
Strain Limit :.02,
Strain Rate:.01,
Dim:.375,,

Sample Cycle Information

Point No	Stress Value	Strain Value	Energy H Cycle (lbs*in↑3/in)
0001	+0.1196E+06	+0.2002E−01	+0.1446E+04
0002	−0.8404E+05	−0.2000E−01	+0.1629E+04
0003	+0.1161E+06	+0.2005E−01	+0.1852E+04
0004	−0.8359E+05	−0.1998E−01	+0.1622E+04
0005	+0.1140E+06	+0.2005E−01	+0.1808E+04
0006	−0.8333E+05	−0.2012E−01	+0.1445E+04
0007	+0.1126E+06	+0.2002E−01	+0.1758E+04

Sample Data Output

Test Demo   14 Feb 70
No Reversals = 0007
Total Energy =+0.1155E+05

Ave. Strain=+0.2289E−01
RMS=+0.2141E−01
Area =+0.1104E+00

Software Program 3 — Random Program (RP)

This program can be used when random load reversal points are needed (Fig. 101). The operator specifies the loading rate and the limits of the load reversal points and the computer program generates the random reversal points as needed.

At each reversal point, the program accumulates the reversal strain and the square of the reversal strain. At program termination the total number of reversals, the average strain, and root mean square of the strain are recorded on the teletype.

In addition, the reversal stress and reversal strains are printed on the teletype for as many reversals as possible.

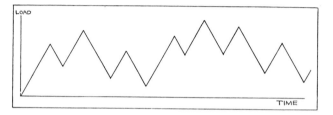

FIG. 101—*"Random walk" fatigue test program.*

Input Parameters

1. Random or constant amplitude.
2. Mean level or reversals.
3. Maximum amplitude of the reversals.
4. Load rate.
5. Specimen area.

Data Output

For as many reversals as possible the following data is recorded on the teletype.

1. Reversal numbers.
2. Reversal stress.
3. Reversal strain.

At test termination, the following data is recorded on the teletype.

1. Total number of reversals.
2. Average reversal strain.
3. Root mean square of the reversal strain.

Software Program 4—Neuber Control (NEUB)

This program provides a means to determine the fatigue life of a notched specimen by testing a smooth specimen. The computer has as its primary inputs a loading history of the notched specimen (ΔS values). By use of the Neuber control the smooth specimen undergoes the same stress-strain history as the notched root material and fails (develops a significant crack) at aproximately the same life.

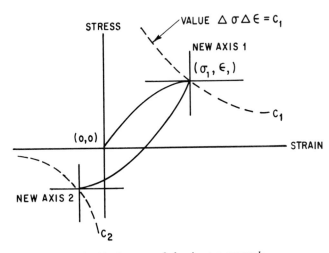

FIG. 102—*Neuber control showing two reversals.*

The computer computes

$$C_j = \frac{(K_f \cdot \Delta S_j)^2}{E}$$

controls strain, and also computes the product $|\sigma_0 - \sigma_i| \cdot |\varepsilon_0 - \varepsilon_i| = \Delta\sigma_i \cdot \Delta\varepsilon_i$ until equal to C_j, where σ_0, ε_0 are the stress-strain at the previous reversal point, and σ_j, ε_i are the current readings of stress and strain (Fig. 102). When the strain direction is reversed and $\sigma_i \rightarrow \sigma_0$, $\varepsilon_i \rightarrow \varepsilon_0$. This procedure is repeated until the smooth specimen develops a significant crack as determined by the operator.

Input Parameters

1. S_j for $j = 1, \ldots, N$ where $N \leqslant 50$.
2. The constant $K_f{}^2/E$.
3. Strain rate.
4. Specimen area.
5. The ΔS_j values.

Data Output

For each reversal:

1. Stress.
2. Strain.
3. Reversal number.

At end of test:

1. Number of reversals to failure.

Sample Input

Neuber's Analysis

Load,ext,stroke,aux:4000,.05,,,
Id:Test A
Control:Load
Dim:.25,,
K:1E-7,
S Values A(N<=24):
2000,-1000,1E50
S Values B (N<=24)
3000,-2000,1E50
Strain Rate:.0004
Direction:Up
Ready

Sample Output

Rev No	Stress	Strain
+.100000E+01	+.118894E+06	+.175134E−01
+.200000E+01	−.368008E+05	+.410356E−02
+.300000E+01	+.117302E+06	+.175867E−01
+.400000E+01	−.403393E+05	+.429897E—02
+.500000E+01	+.115356E+06	+.177332E—01
+.600000E+01	−.417547E+05	+.449438E—02
+.700000E+01	+.114560E+06	+.177821E−01
+.800000E+01	−.438778E+05	+.449438E−02
+.899999E+01	+.113056E+06	+.177332E−01
+.100000E+02	−.439663E+05	+.449438E−02
+.109999E+02	+.112967E+06	+.177332E−01
+.120000E+02	−.452933E+05	+.449438E−02
+.129999E+02	+.112348E+06	+.177088E−01
+.140000E+02	−.452933E+05	+.449438E−02
+.150000E+02	+.111817E+06	+.177332E−01
+.160000E+02	−.460010E+05	+.451880E−02

Rev. No	Stress	Strain
+.170000E+02	+.111552E+06	+.177088E−01
+.180000E+02	−.467087E+05	+.451880E−02
+.189999E+02	+.110844E+06	+.177332E−01
+.200000E+02	−.474164E+05	+.449438E−02
+.210000E+02	+.110137E+06	+.177088E−01
+.219999E+02	−.475933E+05	+.449438E−02
+.230000E+02	+.109694E+06	+.177088E−01
+.240000E+02	−.481241E+05	+.449438E−02
+.250000E+02	+.109606E+06	+.177088E−01
+.259999E+02	−.481241E+05	+.449438E−02
+.269999E+02	+.109694E+06	+.177332E−01
+.280000E+02	−.481241E+05	+.449438E−02
+.290000E+02	+.109075E+06	+.177088E−01
+.300000E+02	−.483010E+05	+.449438E−02

Software Program 5—Low Cycle Fatigue With Random Option (RLCF)

This program has two options: constant amplitude and random amplitude, see Fig. 103. In constant amplitude the reversal strains are constant and in random amplitude the reversal strains are determined by a pseudo random number generator.

The computer controls strain and compute and type out for each half cycle the reversal stress, reversal strain, and energy. At specimen failure, the number of reversals to failure, total energy, average reversal strain, and root square mean of the peaks is printed on the teletype.

Input Parameters

1. Range constants of load cell and extensometer.
2. Date.
3. Identification.
4. Select random option, yes or no.
5. Strain limit.
6. Strain rate.
7. Specimen area.

Data Output

For each reversal, the following data are presented.

1. Reversal stress.
2. Reversal strain.
3. Energy per half cycle.
4. Reversal number.

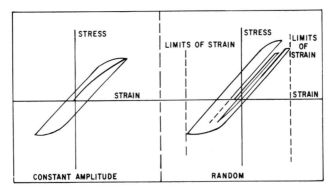

FIG. 103—*Stress versus strain for low-cycle fatigue.*

Total energy is printed out after every 10th reversal point is printed out. At specimen failure the following data is presented.

1. Total number of reversal.
2. Total energy to failure.
3. Average reversal strain.
4. Root square mean of peaks.

Sample Data Input

Random Low Cycle Fatigue
Range Constants:
20000,1000,4000,2000,.05,.05,.05,.05,
Date :Tes←14 Feb 70[4]
I.D. :Test Demo
Random :No
Strain Limit :.02,
Strain Rate:.01,
Dim:.375,,

Sample Cycle Information

Point No	Stress Value	Strain Value	Energy H Cycle (lbs*In↑3/In)
0001	+0.1196E+06	+0.2002E−01	+0.1446E+04
0002	−0.8404E+05	−0.2000E−01	+0.1629E+04
0003	+0.1161E+06	+0.2005E−01	+0.1852E+04
0004	−0.8359E+05	−0.1998E−01	+0.1622E+04
0005	+0.1140E+06	+0.2005E−01	+0.1808E+04
0006	−0.8333E+05	−0.2012E−01	+0.1445E+04
0007	+0.1126E+06	+0.2002E−01	+0.1758E+04

[4] This is an example of an error by the operator being corrected by the use of the arrow signal.

Sample Data Output

Test Demo   14 Feb 70
No Reversals =0007
Total Energy = +0.1155E+05
Ave. Strain= +0.2289E−01
RMS= +0.2141E−01
Area = +0.1104E+00

Software Program 6 — Fatigue Testing Using a Flight-by-Flight Profile

This program is designed to apply a predetermined random or non-random loading history to a component. The program requires four data tables (Endpoint, Mission, Flight, and Oddball) to execute the loading history. These tables can individually be of varied length but their combined length cannot exceed the core limitations of the program (Fig. 104). A total of 1503 locations are available for storing data.

1. Each end point table entry (load level plus time) occupies two locations.
2. Each mission table entry (end point reference plus ratio) occupies two locations.
3. Each oddball table entry (end point reference) occupies one location.
4. Each flight by flight entry (mission reference) occupies one location.

A typical profile might be determined in the following manner.

(a) Fifty distinct end points and times.
(b) Six unique missions using any of the 50 distinct end points in any sequence and the ratio to output the end point. If the ratio is 2, then this end point is applied every second time this mission occurs in the flight.
(c) A flight is defined as a sequence of missions.
(d) Ten oddball missions are defined as a sequence of end points.

The profile is applied in the following manner.

(a) The flight is applied followed by oddball mission No. 1.
(b) The flight is applied again followed by oddball mission No. 2.
(c) (a) and (b) are repeated for oddball missions Nos. 3 through 10.

Other features of the program include the following.

1. Profile is stored in computer memory and, therefore, can be repeated without reading the input tapes again.
2. Null-pacing between the feedback and command.
3. Automatic determination of specimen failure.
4. Haversine waveform between end point.
5. Frequency range from approximately 0.5 to 50 Hz.

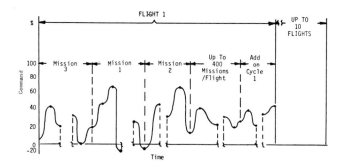

FIG. 104—*An example of a multiple-mission flight-by-flight test program.*

6. Software counters for:

(*a*) mission number, and

(*b*) end point within mission counter.

Input Parameters

1. Scale factors to convert end point units to load readings.
2. Fifty end points and times.
3. Sequence of end points and ratio of each end point for each mission.
4. Eight end points for each of the 10 oddball missions.
5. Sequence of missions to determine a flight.

Output Data

1. End of each flight is indicated with a type-out.
2. At specimen failure, the number of missions, and the number of end points of that mission are typed out.

Equipment

1. A minicomputer or equivalent and a teletype device.
2. A data/control processor with one command channel and one data acquisition channel.
3. Load cell for null-pacing.

11.5 Analog Computers

The primary difference between a digital and analog computer system is that the analog output is continuous and does not require the time interval to compute the next step in the (digital) output waveform. The analog computer can take the input data, in the form of voltages proportional to load, strain, deflection, etc., perform the necessary programmed

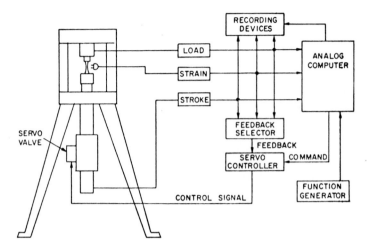

FIG. 105—*Closed loop system with analog computer* [54].

operations, and output a continuous command signal into the control loop (Fig. 105).

Hence, the analog computers can be incorporated into a test system with no significant interface problems to provide some unique test capabilities. Compound parameters involving simple arithmetic combination of simple signals can be synthesized by the analog computer to yield a command signal based on derivation. For example, a simple analog computer can be used to convert diametral measurements of an hour-glass specimen to an equivalent axial strain for control-loop purposes. Another example would involve setting up unusual limits between which a fatigue signal may be cycled (for example, plastic strain limits, equal elastic-plastic strain—Fig. 106) can result in information previously almost impossible to gather at a practical rate. An interesting example is given in Ref *54*, of the use of this device to maximize the speed (frequency) of a servocontrolled test system.

11.6 Hybrid Systems

The use of both a digital and an analog computer for control and data acquisition purposes can produce a hybrid system that utilizes the advantages of both computer types. For example, the waveform generated by the analog system can be cycled between limits prescribed by the digital system. The utilization of the analog system to generate the output waveform permits the digital system to perform the data acquisition and computations necessary for the generation of the next load or strain limit.

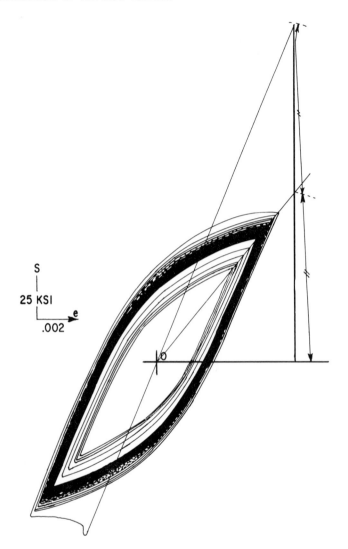

FIG. 106—*Stress-strain plot of SAE 1045 steel in which the elastic and plastic strain ranges are equal for each reversal. Both the stress and total strain ranges change as the material softens* [54].

11.7 Data Acquisition

An earlier development in the application of computers to fatigue testing was the conversion of test output to meaningful scientific information. Such matters as converting from test machine scales (volts, percent of range, etc.) to engineering units (pounds per square inch, metric tons per square millimeter, etc.) can be accomplished quickly. The use of a digital computer for this function certainly can extend the type and quantity of data that can be sampled.

At the completion of a fatigue test, the operator can choose what he wants done with the test data. He can have only significant parameters printed out, the complete test summarized on hard copy, or have the data put on punched or magnetic tape. It is even possible to have the data automatically fed to a central computer for analysis.

With conventional material test sytems, test results are presented on an X-Y recorder, strip-chart recorder, or an oscilloscope, but the data are no more accurate than these devices. Digital data acquisition techniques give inherently better resolution and accuracy (better than 0.1 percent). It is also possible to store correction curves in the system to compensate for nonlinear transducers.

11.8 Conclusions

In summary, there are advantages and disadvantages to both analog and digital computer control of fatigue tests. The analog method is cheaper, simpler, easier to interface with traditional (analog) test equipment, and easier to program. Data presentation is usually graphical.

Digital control involves more expense, is more complex, but also more versatile. Converters are needed to control analog test machines. Data storage is simple and data presentation is essentially alphanumeric without sophisticated peripheral plotter equipment. Cumulative operations are usually much more accurate with digital control, and the possibility of connecting a dedicated fatigue machine computer with a terminal of a large computer make the capability of the digital system virtually unlimited.

Whether one uses a minicomputer or a large-scale facility, computer-controlled testing will resolve itself in the following way. The on-line everyday functioning of the test system will remain in the hands of the system's own private minicomputer. This device will, however, be able automatically to call upon the services of a terminal from the large-scale computer facility for data manipulation, etc. In this way, the large-scale computer will carry out all those functions which do not require performing on-line, and which are too complex for the limited storage capability of the test system's minicomputer.

References

[46] Skoe, R. E. and Swanson, S. R. in *Advanced Testing Techniques, ASTM STP 476,* American Society for Testing and Materials, 1970, pp. 59-78.

[47] Conle, F. A. and Topper, T. H., "Automated Fatigue Testing," *MTS Closed Loop Magazine,* Winter 1971.

[48] Martin, L. M. and Churchill, R. W., "Interfacing the Computer to a Materials Test System," presented at SESA Spring Meeting, Philadelphia, 13-16 May 1969.

[49] Collins, J. C., "The Computer in the Testing Laboratory," *Experimental Mechanics,* Vol. 10, No. 2, Feb. 1970.

[50] Faris, F. G., Adams, C. H., and Bruce, R. W., "Automated Material Testing System," presented at the Spring Meeting, Society for Experimental Stress Analysis (SESA), 7-10 May 1968.

[51] Martin, J. F., Topper, T. H., and Sinclair, G. M., *Materials Research and Standards,* Feb. 1971, pp. 23-50.

[52] Dowling, N. E., "Fatigue Failure Predictions for Complicated Stress-Strain Histories," T+AM Report 337, University of Illinois, Urbana, Jan. 1971.

[53] Stadnick, S. J. and Morrow, JoDean, "Techniques for Smooth Specimen Simulation of the Fatigue Behavior of Notched Members," presented at the ASTM-NMAB Symposium, Anaheim, Calif., April 1971.

[54] Richards, F. D. and Wetzel, R. M., "Mechanical Testing of Materials Using an Analog Computer, Report SR 70-126, Scientific Research Staff, Ford Motor Co.

Appendix A—Nomenclature

In this appendix, the ASTM Definitions of Terms Relating to Fatigue Testing and the Statistical Analysis of Fatigue Data (E 206-72) is reproduced in its entirety, followed by a brief listing of terms used in transducer technology.

ASTM E 206-72

1. Scope

1.1 These definitions cover the principal terms and symbols relating to fatigue testing and the statistical analysis of fatigue data.

2. Index of Terms

2.1 The definitions appear in the following sections:

A. General

For the following definitions see ASTM Definitions E 6, Terms Relating to Methods of Mechanical Testing.[2]

Term

mechanical properties
mechanical testing
strain
stress
stress-strain diagram

B. Definitions Relating to Fatigue Tests and Test Methods

C. Definitions Relating to Statistical Analysis of Fatigue Data

[1] These definitions are under the jurisdiction of ASTM Committee E-9 on Fatigue.

Current edition approved May 1, 1972. Published June 1972. Originally published as E 206 – 62 T. Replaces E 206 – 66.

[2] Annual Book of ASTM Standards, Parts 27, 31.

A. General Definitions

Note—The general terms listed in Section 2 under the Index of Terms are defined in Definitions E 6.

D. Tension, Compression, Shear, and Torsion Testing

For the following definitions, see Definitions E 6:

Term

angular strain
axial strain
biaxial stress
chord modulus
compression modulus
compressive strength
compressive stress
ductility
elastic constants
elastic limit
elongation
fracture stress
gage length
initial tangent modulus
linear strain
macrostrain
malleability
mechanical hysteresis
mechanical properties
mechanical testing
microstrain
modulus of elasticity
modulus of rigidity
modulus of rupture in bending
modulus of rupture in torsion
multiaxial stress
nominal stress
normal stress
Poisson's ratio
principal stress (normal)
proportional limit
reduction of area
secant modulus
set
shear fracture
shear modulus
shear strain
shear strength
shear stress
strain
stress
stress-strain diagram
tangent modulus

B. Definitions Relating to Fatigue Tests and Test Methods

3. fatigue (Note 1)—the process of progressive localized permanent structural change occurring in a material subjected to conditions which produce fluctuating stresses and strains at some point or points and which may culminate in cracks or complete fracture after a sufficient number of fluctuations (Note 2).

Note 1—In glass technology static tests of considerable duration are called "static fatigue" tests, a type of test generally designated as stress-rupture (see Definitions E 6, Section 46).

Note 2—Fluctuations may occur both in stress and with time (frequency), as in the case of "random vibration".

4. fatigue life, N—the number of cycles of stress or strain of a specified character that a given specimen sustains before failure of a specified nature occurs.

5. corrosion fatigue—fatigue aggravated by simultaneous corrosion.

The following definitions 6 to 21, inclusive, apply to those cases where the conditions imposed upon a specimen result or are assumed to result in uniaxial principal stresses or strains which fluctuate in magnitude. Multiaxial stress, sequential loading, and random loading require more rigorous definitions which are, at present beyond the scope of this section.

6. stress cycle—the smallest segment of the stress-time function which is repeated periodically.

7. maximum stress, S_{max} [FL^{-2}]—the stress having the highest algebraic value in the stress cycle, tensile stress being considered positive and compressive stress negative. In this definition as well as in others that follow, the nominal stress is used most commonly.

8. minimum stress, S_{min} [FL^{-2}]—the stress having the lowest algebraic value in the cycle, tensile stress being considered positive and compressive stress negative.

9. mean stress (or steady component of stress), S_m [FL^{-2}]—the algebraic average of the maximum and minimum stresses in one cycle, that is,

$$S_m = (S_{max} + S_{min})/2$$

10. range of stress, S [FL^{-2}]—the algebraic difference between the maximum and minimum stresses in one cycle, that is

$$S_r = S_{max} - S_{min}$$

11. stress amplitude (or variable component of stress), S_a [FL^{-2}]—one half the range of stress, that is

$$S_a = S_r/2 = (S_{max} - S_{min})/2$$

12. stress ratio, A or R—the algebraic ratio of two specified stress values in a stress cycle. Two commonly used stress ratios are: The ratio of the alternating stress amplitude to the mean stress, that is,

$$A = S_a/S_m$$

and the ratio of the minimum stress to the maximum stress, that is,

$$R = S_{min}/S_{max}$$

13. S-N diagram—a plot of stress against the number of cycles to failure. The stress can be S_{max}, S_{min}, or S_a. The diagram indicates the S-N relationship for a specified value of S_m, A, or R and a specified probability of survival. For N a log scale is almost always used. For S a linear scale is used most often, but a log scale is sometimes used.

14. stress cycles endured, n—the number of cycles of a specified character (that produce fluctuating stress and strain) which a specimen has endured at any time in its stress history.

15. fatigue strength at N cycles, S_N [FL^{-2}]— A hypothetical value of stress for failure at exactly N cycles as determined from an S-N diagram. The value of S_N thus determined is subject to the same conditions as those which apply to the S-N diagram.

NOTE—The value of S_N which is commonly found in the literature is the hypothetical value of S_{max}, S_{min}, or S_a at which 50 percent of the specimens of a given sample could survive N stress cycles in which $S_m = 0$. This is also known as the median fatigue strength for N cycles (see Section 24).

16. fatigue limit, S_f [FL^{-2}]—the limiting value of the median fatigue strength as N becomes very large.

NOTE—Certain materials and environments preclude the attainment of a fatigue limit. Values tabulated as "fatigue limits" in the literature are frequently (but not always) values of S_N for 50 percent survival at N cycles of stress in which $S_m = 0$.

17. cycle ratio, C—the ratio of the number of stress cycles, n, of a specified character to the hypothetical fatigue life, N, obtained from the S-N diagram, for stress cycles of the same character, that is, $C = n/N$.

18. theoretical stress concentration factor (or stress concentration factor) K_t—the ratio of the greatest stress in the region of a notch or other stress concentrator as determined by the theory of elasticity (or by experimental procedures that give equivalent values) to the corresponding nominal stress.

NOTE—The theory of plasticity should not be used to determine K.

19. fatigue notch factor, K_f—the ratio of the fatigue strength of a specimen with no stress concentration to the fatigue strength at the same number of cycles with stress concentration for the same conditions.

NOTE—In specifying K_f it is necessary to specify the geometry and the values of S_{max}, S_m, and N for which it is computed.

20. fatigue notch sensitivity, q—a measure of the degree of agreement between K_f and K_t.

NOTE—The definition of fatigue notch sensitivity is $q = (K_f - 1)/(K_t - 1)$.

21. constant life fatigue diagram—a plot (usually on rectangular coordinates) of a family of curves, each of which is for a single fatigue life, N, relating S_a, S_{max} and/or S_{min} to the mean stress S_m. The constant life fatigue diagram is generally derived from a family of S-N curves each of which represents a different stress ratio (A or R) for a 50 percent probability of survival.

C. Definitions Relating to Statistical Analysis of Fatigue Data

22. median fatigue life—the middlemost of the observed fatigue life values, arranged in order of magnitude, of the individual specimens in a group tested under identical conditions. In the case where an even number of specimens are tested it is the average of the two middlemost values.

Note—The use of the sample median instead of the arithmetic mean (that is, the average) is usually preferred.

Note—In the literature, the abbreviated term "fatigue life" usually has meant the median fatigue life of the group. However, when applied to a collection of data without further qualification the term "fatigue life" is ambiguous.

23. fatigue life for p percent survival—an estimate of the fatigue life that p percent of the population would attain or exceed at a given stress level. The observed value of the median fatigue life estimates the fatigue life for 50 percent survival. Fatigue life for p percent survival values, where p is any number, such as 95, 90, etc., may also be estimated from the individual fatigue life values.

24. median fatigue strength at N cycles [FL^{-2}]—an estimate of the stress level at which 50 percent of the population would survive N cycles.

Note—The estimate of the median fatigue strength is derived from a particular point of the fatigue life distribution, since there is no test procedure by which a frequency distribution of fatigue strengths at N cycles can be directly observed.

Note—This is a special case of the more general definition (Section 25).

25. fatigue strength for p percent survival at N cycles [FL^{-2}]—an estimate of the stress level at which p percent of the population would survive N cycles; p may be any number, such as 95, 90, etc.

Note—The estimates of the fatigue strengths for p percent survival values are derived from particular points of the fatigue life distribution, since there is no test procedure by which a frequency distribution of fatigue strengths at N cycles can be directly observed.

26. fatigue limit for p percent survival [FL^{-2}]—the limiting value of fatigue strength for

p percent survival as N becomes very large; p may be any number, such as 95, 90, etc. (Note 5, Section 16).

27. S-N curve for 50 percent survival—a curve fitted to the median values of fatigue life at each of several stress levels. It is an estimate of the relationship between applied stress and the number of cycles-to-failure that 50 percent of the population would survive.

Note—This is a special case of the more general definition (Section 28).

Note—In the literature, the abbreviated term "S-N Curve" usually has meant either the S-N curve drawn through the means (averages) or the medians (50 percent values) for the fatigue life values. Since the term "S-N Curve" is ambiguous, it should be used in technical papers only when adequately described.

28. S-N curve for p percent survival—a curve fitted to the fatigue life for p percent survival values at each of several stress levels. It is an estimate of the relationship between applied stress and the number of cycles-to-failure that p percent of the population would survive. p may be any number, such as 95, 90, etc.

Note—Caution should be used in drawing conclusions from extrapolated portions of the S-N curves. In general, the S-N curves should not be extrapolated beyond observed life values.

29. response curve for N cycles—a curve fitted to observed values of percentage survival at N cycles for several stress levels, where N is a preassigned number such as 10^6, 10^7, etc. It is an estimate of the relationship between applied stress and the percentage of the population that would survive N cycles.

Note—Values of the median fatigue strength at N cycles and the fatigue strength for p percent survival at N cycles may be derived from the response curve for N cycles if p falls within the range of the percent survival values actually observed.

Note—Caution should be used in drawing conclusions from extrapolated portions of the response curves. In general, the curves should not be extrapolated to other values of p.

30. population (or universe)—the hypothetical collection of all possible test specimens that could be prepared in the specified way from the material under consideration.

31. sample—the specimens selected from the population for test purposes.

NOTE—The method of selecting the sample determines the population about which statistical inference or generalization can be made.

32. group—the specimens tested at one time, or consecutively, at one stress level. A group may comprise one or more specimens.

33. frequency distribution—the way in which the frequencies of occurrence of members of a population, or a sample, are distributed according to the values of the variable under consideration.

34. parameter—a constant (usually unknown) defining some property of the frequency distribution of a population, such as, a population median or a population standard deviation.

35. statistic—a summary value calculated from the observed values in a sample.

36. estimation—a procedure for making a statistical inference about the numerical values of one or more unknown population parameters from the observed values in a sample.

37. estimate—the particular value, or values, of a parameter computed by an estimation procedure for a given sample.

38. point estimate—the estimate of a parameter given by a single statistic.

39. sample median—the middle value when all observed values in a sample are arranged in order of magnitude if an odd number of samples are tested. If the sample size is even, it is the average of the two middlemost values. It is a point estimate of the population median, or 50 percent point.

40. sample average (arithmetic mean)—the sum of all the observed values in a sample divided by the sample size. It is a point estimate of the population mean.

41. sample variance, s^2—the sum of the squares of the differences between each observed value and the sample average divided by the sample size minus one. It is a point estimate of the population variance.

NOTE—This value of s^2 provides both an unbiased point estimate of the population variance and a statistic that is used in computing the interval estimates and several test-statistics (Sections 44 and 52). Some texts define s^2 as "the sum of the squares of the differences between each observed value and the sample average divided by the sample size" but this statistic is not as useful.

42. sample standard deviation, s—the square root of the sample variance. It is a point estimate of the population standard deviation, a measure of the "spread" of the frequency distribution of a population.

NOTE—This value of s provides a statistic that is used in computing interval estimates and several test-statistics (Sections 44 and 52). For small sample sizes, s underestimates the population standard deviation. (See the ASTM Manual on Quality Control of Materials, *STP 15C*, or texts on statistics for an unbiased estimate of the standard deviation of a normal population.)

43. sample percentage—the percentage of observed values between two stated values of the variable under consideration. It is a point estimate of the percentage of the population between the same two stated values. (One stated value may be $-\infty$ or $+\infty$.)

44. interval estimate—the estimate of a parameter given by two statistics, defining the end points of an interval.

45. confidence interval—an interval estimate of a population parameter computed so that the statement "the population parameter lies in this interval" will be true, on the average, in a stated proportion of the times such statements are made.

46. confidence limits—the two statistics that define a confidence interval.

47. confidence level (or coefficient)—the stated proportion of the times the confidence interval is expected to include the population parameter.

48. tolerance interval—an interval computed so that it will include at least a stated percentage of the population with a stated probability.

49. tolerance limits—the two statistics that define a tolerance interval. (One value may be $-\infty$ or $+\infty$.)

50. tolerance level—the stated probability that the tolerance interval includes at least the stated percentage of the population. It is not the same as a confidence level but the term confidence level is frequently associated with tolerance intervals.

51. significant—statistically significant. An effect or difference between populations is said to be present if the value of a test-statistic is significant, that is, lies outside of predetermined limits.

NOTE—An effect which is statistically significant may or may not have engineering signifi-cance.

52. test-statistic—a function of the observed values in a sample that is used in a test of significance.

53. test of significance—a test which, by use of a test-statistic, purports to provide a test of the hypothesis that the effect is absent.

NOTE—The rejection of the hypothesis indi-cates that the effect is present.

54. significance level—the stated probability (risk) that a given test of significance will reject the hypothesis that a specified effect is absent when the hypothesis is true.

D. TENSION, COMPRESSION, SHEAR, AND TORSION TESTING

NOTE—The terms on tension, compression, shear, and torsion testing listed in Section 2 under the Index of Terms are defined in ASTM Defini-tions E 6, Terms Relating to Methods of Mechani-cal Testing.[2]

APPENDIX

A1. SYMBOLS AND ABBREVIATIONS

A1.1 The following symbols and abbreviations are frequently used in lieu of or along with the terms cov-ered by the preceding definitions. For stress, the use of S with appropriate lower case subscripts is preferred for general purposes; for mathematical analysis the use of Greek symbols is generally preferred.

Symbol	Term	Symbol	Term
A	area of cross section, stress ratio	S_{cy}	compressive yield strength
C	cycle ratio	S_m	mean stress
c	distance from centroid to outermost fiber	S_{max}	maximum stress
D or d	diameter	S_{min}	minimum stress
E	modulus of elasticity in tension or compres-sion	S_N	fatigue strength at N cycles
ϵ (epsilon)	strain	S_r	range of stress
F	force	S_s (or τ)	shear stress
ft · lbf	a unit of work[3]	S_t	tensile stress
G	modulus of elasticity in shear	S_{ty}	tensile yield strength
γ (gamma)	shear strain	S_u	tensile strength
I	moment of inertia	σ (sigma)	standard deviation, nominal stress[6]
i	subscript denoting i th term	$\hat{\sigma}$	estimate of standard deviation
in · lbf	a unit of work[3]	σ^2	variance
J	polar moment of inertia	σ_x	standard deviation of x
ksi	thousands of pounds-force per square inch or kips-force per square inch[1]	σ^2_x	variance of x
		T	torque, temperature
K_f	fatigue notch factor	t	time
K_t	theoretical stress concentration factor	τ (tau) or S_s	shear stress
L	length	w	load per unit distance or per unit area
lbf · ft	a unit of torque[3]	w/A	total distributed load for a given area
lbf · in.	a unit of torque[3]	wL	total distributed load for a given length
M	bending moment	W	work or energy
μ (mu)	Poisson's ratio[4]	Z	section modulus[7]
N	fatigue life (number of cycles)		
n	number of stress cycles endured, sample size		
P	concentrated load		
psi	pounds-force per square inch[1]		
p	probability[5]		
q	fatigue notch sensitivity		
R	stress ratio		
s	sample standard deviation		
s^2	sample variance		
S	nominal stress		
S (or σ)	normal stress		
S_a	stress amplitude		
S_c	compressive stress		
S_r	fatigue limit		

[1] Because it is general engineering practice in the USA to use "pound" rather than the technically correct term "pound-force," the symbol "lb" rather than "lbf" may be used in some standards. Similarly, in the abbreviations "ksi" and "psi" the "pound-force" is the unit involved.

[4] ν (nu) is preferred in applied mechanics.

[5] This may be probability of failure or probability of survival; the meaning should be specified.

[6] σ is preferred in applied mechanics but should not be used when statistical treatments are involved.

[7] Many handbooks use S for section modulus, but Z is preferred since S is so widely used for nominal or normal stress.

Transducer Terminology

While it is recognized that a variety of terms are used by manufacturers for product description, a minimum number of key terms have been selected which are necessary to obtain, in a clear, and concise manner, descriptive data to make the ISA Transducer Compendium a valuable reference to those actively engaged in this area of instrumentation.

Measurand and Output

measurand—is the physical quantity, property, or condition which is measured.

measurand range—are the minimum and maximum values of the measurand.

measurand properties—are the inherent properties of the measurand which must be maintained while a transducer operates within a specified range. (These properties are not to be confused with environmental characteristics.) For example, consider a flowmeter measuring the flow rate of water in a pipe. Unless the water pressure is within certain limits the flowmeter will not operate correctly; therefore, the minimum and maximum pressure limits of the water would have to be listed under measurand properties.

operating principle—is the nature of the sensing technique and the transducer principle necessary to sense the measurand and to produce an output signal, for example, bourdon tube, bellows, resistive, capacitive, inductive, etc.

output characteristics—are the nature of the output signal (electrical, pneumatic, hydraulic), output range (s), power output, and output impedance.

sensitivity—is the ratio of full-scale output to full-scale measurand value. (Identify units clearly.)

excitation—is the nature and magnitude of all external energy required for proper transducer operation; this, of course, excludes the measurand. This includes power requirements, comparative circuits, pneumatic or hydraulic pressures, etc.

Operating Characteristics

theoretical transfer function—is the theoretical relation between measurand and output values as determined by inherent principles of operation. It is expressed as common functions, for example, linear, parabolic, logarithmic, sinusoidal, etc.

static error band—is the deviation from the theoretical transfer function under constant environmental conditions. This, of course, includes effects of hysteresis, friction and repeatability, as well as other sources of error which are not due to environmental variations.

Example:

Range	Maximum Error
(percent of full-scale measurand)	(percent of full-scale output)
from 0 to 20	± 6.0
from 20 to 75	± 5.0
from 75 to 100	±10.0

environmental conditions: 25°C

repeatability—is the ability of a transducer to reproduce and output signal when the same measurand value is applied to it three succesive times, under the same conditions and direction. It is expressed as the maximum difference between output readings in terms of percent of full-scale output.

Example

Range	Repeatability
(percent of full-scale measurand)	(percent of full-scale output)

resolution—is the smallest change of measurand that produces a recogniz-able change in output, expressed as a percentage of full-scale measu-rand. Resolution is sometimes referred to as "threshold" in certain specific applications.

Example

Range	Resolution
(percent of full-scale measurand)	(percent of full-scale measurand)
from 0 to 70	0.1
from 70 to 100	0.2

environmental conditions: standard temperature and pressure

overrange—is the maximum magnitude of the measurand that can be applied to a transducer without causing a change in performance beyond the specified tolerances (expressed as percent of full-scale measurand). An overrange factor may sometimes be referred to as "overload" factor.

zero shift—is a displacement of the entire calibration curve expressed as a percent of full-scale output.

time constant—is the time required for the transducer output to reach 63 percent of its final output value as a result of a step change in the measurand.

Environmental Characteristics

environmental ranges—The range of environmental conditions under which a transducer will perform within static error band limits. Typical environmental conditions are temperature, pressure, humidity, acceleration, vibration (includes resonant and natural frequencies), magnetic and electrical effects, shock, noise, and radiation.

environmental effects—Are the changes in output due to change in the environmental conditions, expressed as the change in output (percent of full-scale) per unit of environmental change.

standard temperature and pressure—are 25.0°C (77°F) and one atmosphere (29.92 in. Hg or 14.69 psia), respectively. The standard temperature and pressure condition also includes zero vibration and acceleration.

Physical Characteristics

size—the overall physical dimensions of the transducer.

mounting—the mounting specifications, for example, end clamp, flange, screw, etc.

connections—the type of connections to the transducer, for example, receptacle, solder terminals, threaded inlet, etc.

materials of construction—the principal materials of construction, for example, stainless steel, plastic, etc.

weight—the weight of the transducer and its required auxiliary equipment.

life expectancy—the transducer life expressed in terms of full-scale cycles, or exposure time under operating conditions before the transducer performance exceeds static error band limits.

interchangeability—is the extent to which individual transducers of a model series can be interchanged.

Terminology Related to Readout Equipment Transducers

natural frequency—frequency at which transducer will resonate.

temperature sensitivity—percent of full-scale output per 100°F increase in temperature.

hysteresis—when two separate data points for one certain level of measurand input are compared, one point having been determined, following an increasing input from zero to full range, the other following a decrease in input from full scale to zero, the deviation in output between the two data points is defined as hysteresis.

repeatability—the difference between successive calibrations of the same transducers under identical test conditions is defined as repeatability. At least three complete full-scale transducer cycles for most transducers are applied prior to starting the initial calibration.

sensitivity—transducer full scale output per volt of excitation.

excitation—the nature and magnitude of all external energy required for proper transducer operation.

resolution—the smallest change of measurand that produces a recognizable change in output expressed as percent of full-scale measurand—sometimes referred to as "threshold."

time constant—the time required for the transducer output to reach 63 percent of its final output value as a result of a step change in the measurand. Usually only applicable in first order system.

dependent linearity—maximum deviation from a straight line drawn through the zero and full output points. Given as a percent of full output.

independent linearity—maximum deviation from a straight line that is positioned on the transfer characteristic in such a manner as to result in the smallest deviation.

Appendix B—Specifications in the Field of Fatigue Testing

This chapter will list the various specifications relating to fatigue testing in general, and fatigue tests for various products.

International Standards

The ISO Standards and Recommendations

The following countries are members of the International Organization for Standardization (ISO):

Australia	France	Poland
Austria	Germany	Portugal
Belgium	Greece	Romania
Bulgaria	Hungary	Spain
Burma	India	Sweden
Canada	Ireland	Switzerland
Chile	Italy	Turkey
Czechoslovakia	Japan	United Kingdom
Denmark	Morocco	United States of America
Egypt	Netherlands	U.S.S.R.
Finland	New Zealand	Yugoslavia
	Norway	

This group has prepared a number of recommendations and standards relating to fatigue (Table 2).

ISO Recommendation R373—General Principles for Fatigue Testing of Metals.
ISO Recommendation 733E (Draft)—Methods of Fatigue Testing Part 3: Axial Load Fatigue Testing.
ISO Recommendation 1350 (Draft)—Rotating Bar Bending Fatigue Testing.
ISO Recommendation 1352 (Draft)—Torsional Stress Fatigue Testing.

Work is presently underway on a proposal for Dynamic Force Calibration of Direct Stress Fatigue Machines.
The member bodies (the national standards organizations of the

TABLE 2—*ISO proposals for fatigue testing.*

Method	Rotating Bending	Axial Loading	Torsion Loading
Scope	0.02 to 0.5-in. diameter circular cross-section, unnotched specimens tested in air at room temperature	0.05 to 1.0 sq. in. area—rectangular cross-section	
Specimen Size	figures, dimensions, and tolerances		
Specimen Preparation	machine such that work-hardening of surface is minimized, avoid overheating. Detailed procedures for turning, milling (in case of axial loading), grinding, surface finish, and storage.		
Specimen Mounting	coaxiality of machine and specimen		
	allowable eccentricity	avoid twisting specimen	avoid bending stresses
Test Frequency	1000 to 12 000 cpm	250 to 18 000 cpm	depends on machine
Load Application	bring up to speed, then apply moment	apply mean, then fluctuating component, monitor during test. *Calibrate dynamically.*	
Accuracy	$\pm 1\%$ of nominal moment	dynamic mean and range, $\pm 3\%$ of their nominal value or $\pm \frac{1}{2}\%$ machine capacity, whichever is greater.	
Failure Criterion	complete fracture		
Run-out	10^7 cycles—structural steels. 10^8 cycles—other steels, nonferrous metals.		
Presentation of Results	graphic presentation as per R373. Include details of specimen material and condition, type of specimen and machine, frequency, temperature and relative humidity (if outside range of 50 to 70%), criterion of failure, any deviations from required conditions (and stress ratio or mean stress in case of axial or torsional loading).		

countries just listed) can approve or oppose these recommendations. Specific information on these specifications should be obtained from the appropriate national standards organization (for example, in the United States, National Bureau of Standards; in the United Kingdom, the British Standards Institution). The British Standards Institution serves as the secretariat for many of these specifications, while the main secretariat is:

ISO Central Secretariat
1, rue de Varembe
1211 Geneve 20
Switzerland

National Standards

West Germany

The German Standards (DIN) are well developed and cover aspects of fatigue test methods as well as special product-oriented tests. They can be obtained from:

Deutscher Normenausschuss (DNA)
1 Berlin 30
Burggrafenstrasse 4-7

Most of the relevant standards are available in English as well, though only the German language versions are official.

DIN 50100: Testing of Materials, fatigue test, definitions, symbols, procedure, evaluation.
DIN 51228: Fatigue testing machines, definitions, general requirements.

The United Kingdom

The British Standards Institution (British Standards House, 2 Park Street, London W.1, England), developed the following standards in the field of fatigue testing. These have been approved by the Mechanical Engineering Industry Standards Committee and endorsed by the Chairman of the U.K. Engineering Divisional Council.

Methods of Fatigue Testing Parts 1-5, British Standards Institution B.S. 3518

Part 1	1962	General Principles.
Part 2	1962	Rotating Bending Fatigue Tests.
Part 3	1963	Direct Stress Fatigue Tests.
Part 4	1963	Torsional Stress Fatigue Tests.
Part 5	1966	Guide to the Application of Statistics.

The United States

While there are numerous specifications relating to fatigue, many of them emanate from professional bodies directly, rather than from governmental institutions. There is, however, a trend at present, for many of these specifications to have complete governmental backing from a legal viewpoint.

Military Handbook 5—"Strength of Metal Aircraft Elements." This document was prepared and is maintained by the U.S. Department of Defense with the assistance of the Federal Aviation Agency. It contains data on material properties required of manufacturers by the U.S. Government for military equipment. It contains fatigue data, but not detailed fatigue specifications at present.

American Standards Institute (USASI)—The organization has been active in converting professional specifications into federal specifications.

A number of "codes" bear on fatigue and flaw growth implicitly:

Welding Society Pressure Vessel Research Committee
American Petroleum Institute (API)
American Gas Association

The following professional groups have specifications of materials and products some of which bear on fatigue:

Society of Automotive Engineers AMS Committee
ASME Metals Engineering Division, Code Committees

American Society for Testing and Materials—Work is underway on the development of other test method standards in fatigue; those available are:

ASTM Recommended Practice for Constant Amplitude Axial Fatigue Tests of Metallic Materials (E 466-72T)

ASTM Recommended Practice for Verification of Constant Amplitude Dynamic Loads in an Axial Load Fatigue Testing Machine (3 467-72T)

ASTM Recommended Practice for Presentation of Constant Amplitude Fatigue Test Results for Metallic Materials (E 468-72T)

ASTM Test for Shear Fatigue of Sandwich Core Materials (C 394-62)

ASTM Testing Automotive Hydraulic Brake Hose (D 571-72)

ASTM Tests for Compression Fatigue of Vulcanized Rubber (D 623-67)

ASTM Test for Flexural Fatigue of Plastics by Constant-Amplitude-of-Force (D 671-71)

ASTM Test for Crack Growth of Rubber (D 813-59)

ASTM Specifications and Tests for Latex Foam Rubbers (D 1155-69)

ASTM Specifications and Tests for Flexible Foams Made form Polymers of Copolymers of Vinyl Chloride (D 1565-70)

ASTM Testing Molded Flexible Urethane Foam (D 2406-68)

Appendix C—Professional Society Groups Related to Fatigue Testing

The techniques of fatigue testing draw heavily upon various technical areas which are presently experiencing rapid growth. Computer technology, for example, must be monitored almost weekly to appreciate the possibilities which become available for incorporation into fatigue testing.

Because of these continuing opportunities for improvement, the scientist or engineer concerned with fatigue is well advised to become a member of one or more of the professional groups in fatigue research. This chapter will briefly describe as many of these groups as possible, pointing out the aspects which differentiate them one from another.

International Groups Concerned with Fatigue

The International Committee on Aeronautical Fatigue (ICAF)

The International Committee on Aeronautical Fatigue (ICAF) is composed of one representative of each of ten countries having an interest in aeronautical fatigue. In almost all cases that representative is actively engaged in fatigue research at the national aeronautical research establishment of his country.

The Federation Internationale des Societes d'Ingenieurs des Techniques de l'Automobile (FISITA)

This international organization is a federation of national societies for automotive engineering. While it has no formal subdivision for the subject of fatigue, its meetings, held every two years, are often used by fatigue researchers connected with automotive science to publish their results.

National Organizations

American Organizations

The American Society for Testing and Materials (ASTM)

Committee E-9 on Fatigue

This organization has had a standing committee for fatigue (Committee

E-9) for over 25 years, and in 1949 published their *Manual on Fatigue Testing, STP 91*. Committee E-9 has been the focal point of a very large portion of the fatigue activity in the United States. It has several subcommittees which are restructured from time to time to serve the interests of the members. The scope of this committee is as follows.

Scope

The promotion of research on the nature of fatigue behavior and methods for improving fatigue behavior.

The development of methods for determining fatigue characteristics of simple and *composite* materials, components, processed parts, and complete assemblies.

The development of analytical procedures for interpreting fatigue test results and for designing against fatigue.

The coordination of activities in these areas wherever they might be conducted.

And the standardization of nomenclature, definitions, data evaluation, and methods.

Area of Interest

Included in this scope is any engineering application in which the materials, processed parts, components, or complete assemblies used are subjected to stresses and strains that might result in fatigue damage or failure. Among the *parameters* of interest are:

Environment
Physical deformation mechanisms
Fatigue crack propagation
Fracture
Relation between stress, strain level and life
Behavior of specific materials
Metallurgical considerations
Processing variables
Residual stresses
Stress and strain concentrations
Stress analysis (elastic and plastic)
Variable amplitude and random loadings
Joints—methods, fasteners, welds, spot welds
Fretting
Corrosion
Vacuum
Temperature
Statistical analysis

Rolling contact
Speed of testing
Size
Damage detection
Methods of test
Test equipment
Effect of damage accumulation

The present structure is as follows:

Subcommittee .01 Research

The purposes of the Research Subcommittee of E-9 are as follows:

1. To keep membership of the main committee informed of advances in the understanding of fatigue.
2. To promote the development of further understanding of the fatigue process as influenced by both internal (material) and external (load and environment) parameters.
3. To meet these objectives the subcommittee will sponsor symposia on topics of current interest in fatigue research and assist in the publication of the proceedings of such meetings where appropriate.

Subcommittee .02 Papers

The papers subcommittee is concerned with timely and effective presentation and publication of papers in the field of fatigue of materials. To this end it shall,

1. Invite, review, and schedule papers for sessions and conduct these sessions at annual meetings and other occasions except when these functions are delegated to others, such as symposia chairmen.
2. Assist symposia chairmen and others in planning, organizing, and conducting meetings.
3. Review papers submitted for publication and maintain a list of reviewers and their fields of competence.
4. Maintain and improve the quality of papers, of their delivery in meetings, and of their discussion. (An annual award for the best presented paper is made by this subcommittee.)
5. Submit broad plans for sessions and symposia to the executive committee.

Subcommittee .03 Fatigue of Composite Materials

1. Develop standard fatigue test methods and materials specifications for fatigue resistance.

2. Promote research on and an understanding of the mechanisms of fatigue failure in composite materials.
3. Organize and sponsor working-group sessions and technical symposia on fatigue of composite materials.
4. Coordinate committee activities with other technical societies and ASTM committees having an interest in the fatigue of composite materials.
5. Provide a source of expert opinion through subcommittee members on composite fatigue problems.

Subcommittee .04 Apparatus and Test Methods

The activities of Subcommittee .04 may include study, discussion, and investigation of any problems relating to the procedures for testing materials and structures under fluctuating load. The objectives of these activities are to develop and disseminate information that will help to make these procedures more accurate, more reproducible, and more significant.

Subcommittee .05 Structural Fatigue Problems

1. The promotion of research on the nature of structural fatigue behavior and methods for improving structural fatigue behavior and the correlation of this work with work on basic fundamentals.
2. The development of methods for determining the fatigue behavior of structural components and complete assemblies.
3. The development of analytical procedures for interpreting fatigue test results and for designing against fatigue.
4. The development of methods for assessing and/or detecting the fatigue damage incurred by structures.

Subcommittee .06 Statistical Aspects of Fatigue

1. To bring probabilistic and statistical methods of experimental design, data gathering, and analysis within the grasp of the practicing fatigue engineer with the aid of handbooks (91-A).
2. To organize symposia for the dissemination of new and current information.
3. To encourage researchers, material suppliers and designers in the publication and use of statistically meaningful data and parameters.
4. And to oversee the writing and publication of definitions for all subcommittees of Committee E-9.

Current and future areas of interest include: design of experiments, random load fatigue, small sample statistics, proof testing, censoring of data, computer programs for data reduction, reliability, early failure analysis, safety factors and scatter factors, simulation of the interactions between the fatigue process, and environmental effects based on probabilistic considerations.

Subcommittee .08 Fatigue Under Cyclic Strain

Subcommittee .08 is concerned with fatigue under those conditions where strain rather than stress is the controlling variable. Further, the strains of interest are of such a magnitude that macroscopic plastic strains must be considered. In this regime deformation and failure mechanisms, material behavior, property information, testing methods and design are areas of concern, both at high and low temperatures or under cyclic temperatures.

Committee E-24 on Fracture Toughness

This committee is concerned mainly with final rupture or failure of materials, when flaws within the material have reached a critical size, Subcommittee E24.04. Subcritical flaw growth often concerns itself with the growth of flaws due to fatigue loading. This is, of course, fatigue crack propagation and represents part of the area discussed in Chapter 8 of this manual. The scope of this committee is:

Scope

To promote knowledge and advancement in the field of fracture testing by:

1. Promoting research and development on methods for appraisal of the fracture resistance of metals.
2. Developing recommended practices, methods of test, definitions, and nomenclature for fracture testing of metals, exclusive of fatigue testing.
3. Sponsoring technical meetings and symposia independently or in cooperation with other organizations.
4. Coordinating the committee activities with those of other relevant ASTM committees and other organizations.

Subcommittee .01 Fracture Mechanics Test Methods

To implement the functions of Committee E-24 as applied specifically to the development of test methods based directly or indirectly upon fracture mechanics. This includes methods for directly determining parameters defining or describing the stress-crack size conditions under which fracture takes place, and methods for screening and quality control.

Subcommittee .02 Fractography and Associated Microstructures

1. To relate fracture and crack growth properties and micromechanisms to material structural and fractographic features.
2. To advance failure analysis techniques and procedures.
3. To assist the Main and other Subcommittees both in an advisory capacity, and through mutual cooperation in joint Task Groups.

Subcommittee .03 Dynamic Testing

1. To develop test methods for measuring the toughness of metals under dynamic loading conditions.
2. To establish relationships between empirical measures of toughness obtained in dynamic tests and basic fracture mechanics toughness parameters.

Subcommittee .04 Subcritical Crack Growth

1. To promote research on subcritical-crack growth and to develop methods for appraisal of subcritical-crack growth resistance of materials.
2. To develop recommended practices, methods of tests, definitions, and nomenclature for testing of subcritical-crack growth resistance of materials in cooperation with other appropriate ASTM committees, (for example, Committees E-9 and G-1).

Subcommittee .05 Nomenclature and Definitions

To formulate proposed standard nomenclature and definitions that fall within the scope of Committee E-24, and to cooperate with Committee E-8 on Nomenclature and Definitions.

Subcommittee .06 Applications

1. To assess the adequacy of current fracture test methods from an applications standpoint and define industry and government needs for additional test methods. To advise the main and other subcommittees of these needs.
2. To develop improved methods and techniques for applying the results of fracture and subcritical flaw growth tests to the solution of engineering problems and the design of fracture resistant structures.
3. To act as a forum for the exchange of concepts, approaches, and detailed technical information related to the application of fracture test data.

American Society of Civil Engineers (ASCE)

Task Committee on Structural Fatigue

This group of civil engineers is concerned with fatigue, and is subdivided into four areas:

1. Fatigue analyses and theories.
2. Fatigue of members and details.
3. Loading of histories and cumulative damage.
4. Design.

American Society of Mechanical Engineers (ASME)

There are several subcommittees within this group concerned with fatigue.

American Society for Metals (ASM)

This organization, composed primarily of metallurgists, but lately including a growing number of those working with non-metals, often has activities centered around the subject of fatigue.

Society of Automotive Engineers (SAE)

Fatigue Design and Evaluation Committee

This is the location, within the American automotive field, of the group interested in the durability of automobiles and other terrestrial vehicles. This permanent committee has several divisions, the titles of which make them self-explanatory:

1. Cumulative Fatigue Damage Division
2. Fatigue Design Analysis Division (This group is primarily interested in the ways field data may be obtained to permit sound fatigue life analysis.)
3. X-Ray Fatigue Division (X-Rays as a Non-Destructive Test Technique in Fatigue)
4. Inclusion Fatigue Division
5. Mechanical Prestress Division
6. Fracture Control Division (A new division concerned with fracture toughness of automotive materials.)

Additional Groups

In addition to the previous groups, there are several groups which, from time to time, concern themselves with matters involving fatigue.

1. Metal Properties Council
2. Engineering Joint Council
3. ASTM-ASME Joint Committee on Effect of Temperature
       Low Temperature Panel
       Test Methods Panel
4. U.S. National Academy of Engineering
       Materials Advisory Board
       Advisory Group on Fracture
5. U.S. Department of Transportation
       Highway Research Board
6. U.S. Department of Commerce

United Kingdom

The Royal Aeronautical Society

Since 1940 the Royal Aeronautical Society has produced and issued authoritative data on aeronautical engineering and science in the form of data sheets and data memoranda.

The *Aeronautical Series* in this set of publications has six sub-series, of which one is titled "Fatigue."

The aim of these data sheets in fatigue is to provide, in a form convenient to designers and others, information relating to fatigue. The results of much valuable work, both theoretical and practical, are frequently not applied because they are buried in a large number of technical reports which potential users have the time neither to discover nor to read. Further, experience in dealing with certain aspects of fatigue problems is often not suitable as a basis for the writing of conventional technical reports and, in the absence of a suitable publication, such experience disseminates only very slowly. Accordingly, after a survey of the situation by the Society's Structures Committee, a special committee was appointed to examine reports, to correlate and check their conclusions, and to review combined experience in dealing with fatigue problems.